WORKBOOK IN
INTRODUCTORY ECONOMICS

Diagram

Clear ½ 10 crimes mill

Large

Cobbe

Clear

deceased

No raffle

Essay code out al-Avantive.

WORKBOOK IN INTRODUCTORY ECONOMICS

by

Colin Harbury, B.Com., Ph.D.
Professor of Economics, The City University, London

Third Edition

PERGAMON PRESS
OXFORD · NEW YORK · TORONTO · SYDNEY · PARIS · FRANKFURT

U.K.	Pergamon Press Ltd., Headington Hill Hall, Oxford OX3 0BW, England
U.S.A.	Pergamon Press Inc., Maxwell House, Fairview Park, Elmsford, New York 10523, U.S.A.
CANADA	Pergamon Press Canada Ltd., Suite 104, 150 Consumers Rd., Willowdale, Ontario M2J 1P9, Canada
AUSTRALIA	Pergamon Press (Aust.) Pty. Ltd., P.O. Box 544, Potts Point, N.S.W. 2011, Australia
FRANCE	Pergamon Press SARL, 24 rue des Ecoles, 75240 Paris, Cedex 05, France
FEDERAL REPUBLIC OF GERMANY	Pergamon Press GmbH, Hammerweg 6, D-6242 Kronberg-Taunus, Federal Republic of Germany

First edition 1968

Second edition 1974

Third edition 1982

Reprinted 1976, 1978

Reprinted 1984

Library of Congress Cataloging in Publication Data
Harbury, C. D.
Workbook in introductory economics.
1. Economics—Problems, exercises, etc. 2. Great
Britain—Economic conditions—Problems, exercises, etc.
i. Title.
HB74.6H37   1982   330'.076   81-17954
AACR2

British Library Cataloguing in Publication Data
Harbury, Colin
Workbook in introductory economics.
—3rd ed.
1. Economics
I. Title
330   HB171.5
ISBN 0-08-027442-0

In order to make this volume available as economically and as rapidly as possible the typescript has been reproduced in its original form. This method unfortunately has its typographical limitations but it is hoped that they in no way distract the reader.

Printed in Great Britain by A. Wheaton & Co. Ltd., Exeter

Contents

Introduction
(for students, teachers and the self-taught)

Economics can be an exciting subject. But simply reading about general principles in an elementary textbook can be decidedly dull. The material only too often seems dead, not to say indescribably irrelevant.

The secret of bringing the subject to life is to use it, to set your mind to work by applying newly acquired principles to novel situations. This workbook has been designed to help you learn and use economics, to aid in testing your level of understanding and to improve your skill in answering multiple-choice and data-response questions, which are used nowadays in many examinations.

A detailed description of the contents of the book is given in the next section, HOW TO USE THE WORKBOOK. It should be very carefully studied. Briefly, each chapter is divided into four main sections — textual summaries of the ground covered, questions and problems in economic analysis, questions and exercises on the U.K. economy, and essays.

The summaries of the main material dealt with in each chapter are not intended as substitutes for a textbook. They are highly condensed and may send you rushing back to your text for clarification. This raises an important matter. My workbook, unlike many others, is not written to 'accompany' a particular text, but to be suitable for use with the standard ones on the market. I confess to believing that it is highly desirable to encourage students to read more than one textbook in economics, even at an elementary level. The subject-matter of economics is controversial and there is no better way of appreciating this than by observing the different slants of a variety of authors. Moreover, no one has written a perfect textbook and you will often find that a difficult point is clarified by reading more than one explanation of it. Detailed chapter references to a large number of books are given in the workbook to guide your reading in your main text and other sources.

The multiple-choice questions in both the analysis and U.K. economy sections of each chapter are of the standard five-option type. Those on economic theory are of a wide range of difficulty, the easiest usually coming first. The other questions include what are nowadays described as 'data response'. Here they are called problems and exercises. The problems are in the analysis sections. They employ hypothetical data and call for their interpretation, manipulation and application. Some require simple calculations or the drawing of graphs. The choice of numbers has been kept to an absolute minimum so as to emphasize the economic aspects of a question. Inevitably, such problems are unrealistic, a defect that I do not regard as overserious because the second parts of the U.K. economy sections consist of extremely down-to-earth exercises with real data. They are not simply data-response questions since they require the collection of data in the first place. Detailed guidance is given on easily accessible sources and on presentation. Questions are then posed in order to aid in interpretation of the data and to tie in with basic principles of economics. I am convinced that, though such exercises may sometimes be time-consuming, a little elementary 'research' of this kind is virtually essential to get a grasp of the very nature of economics and the problems of working in the subject. Each chapter ends with a selection of essays of varying degrees of difficulty. They tend to emphasize the implications and applications of economic theory.

Finally, there is the question of the level at which the workbook is aimed. I believe that there is no single answer to this question because of the overlap in syllabuses and textbooks used for different examinations. I admitted in the first edition that I had the needs of A-level candidates uppermost in mind. I know, however, that the book has been used by first-year degree students at universities and polytechnics, and also by others preparing for professional exams. The book was designed to be flexible — some questions are quite suitable for O-level candidates — and I can only hope that it will continue to satisfy a variety of needs.

The New Edition
So much has changed since the last edition of this book that I have had to revise it drastically to take account both of changes in the structure of the economy and of theoretical developments. The U.K. economy sections have naturally come in for major updating, and I have substituted about 350 (including over 100 multiple choice) questions for old ones throughout the book.

An important change is in the exercises on the U.K. economy. These have been adapted to give practice in answering data-response questions, which have started to appear in A-level examinations — a welcome development. My approach has been to retain the data collection parts of exercises but to tack on to them questions specifically designed to help in interpreting data and in associating economic problems with basic principles. This is the essence of applied economics and it is never too soon to begin to think in this way. I should add that I have been writing about factual data. Questions involving the manipulation of hypothetical data have always been in the book, in the problems in the analysis sections of each chapter, though they have not been given the 'in-word' title of data response.

In preparing the new edition I should like to record my thanks to the many teachers and students who have written to me over the years with problems relating to material in the old edition. I have found this feedback invaluable. Please continue. I must also acknowledge my gratitude to Dr Robert Cressy, who carefully scrutinized all the new material, making many valuable suggestions and saving me from obscurities and errors. I do not really see the point in adding that any that remain are my responsibility. It is obvious. But is is also the convention, so I do so.

HOW TO USE THE WORKBOOK

This is a workbook to help you learn economics. Answers are provded so that you can test your own progress. All the chapters are organized in the same way, starting with a summary of the material covered, followed by questions on economic analysis and the U.K. economy and by a list of essays. There is no need to stick to the order in the book. It is flexible. For example, if your course begins with national income, start with chapter 5.

I Summaries of Material These are NOT intended as substitutes for your textbook, but to tell you what ground is covered in each chapter. You will find them highly condensed and therefore hard going unless you have already studied the subject-matter elsewhere. Since this workbook was not written to accompany any particular text, I have prepared a reading guide (see pages x to xiii) which gives chapter references to those in common use which are covered in each chapter of this book. If your own text is not very helpful in any area, try to get hold of one of those marked with asterisks, which are especially recommended.

II Analysis These sectiosn contain multiple-choice questions and problems in economic theory.

(a) <u>Multiple-choice questions</u>. Each offers you five alternative answers from which to choose. Usually there is only one correct answer, though it may sometimes be the best of the alternatives. Answers are everywhere provided. If you get stuck, look at the answer, refer back to your textbook and go over the ground again. Try the question again the following day, or later.

It should be emphasized that the questions are not trying to catch you out, but to test your understanding. Direct and normal relationships are emphasized in the analysis, and you are not expected to try to imagine some highly peculiar situations which could conceivably result in a rare conclusion. I hope you will not find ambiguities in the questions, but if you do, consult your teacher for advice (and I should very much like to know about them myself). Remember that some 'wrong' answers may simply not be the best of the alternatives offered, while others are positively erroneous.

I cannot stress too strongly that an important part of the learning process involves understanding why each incorrect option in a multiple-choice question is wrong as well as knowing the right one. This ought to be obvious in cases where the correct option is 'None of the above'. But you are strongly advised to work through every alternative in all questions until you are satisfied that you understand why each incorrect option is faulty.* One final suggestion. If you have had particular difficulty with a question, but think you have finally mastered it, it is quite a good idea to see if you can alter the stem of the question so as to make a different option the correct one.

(b) <u>Problems</u>. These are intended to provide you with additional working material in important areas of economic theory without the inevitable restrictions that are involved with multiple-choice questions. Many involve you in making calculations and working with graphs and diagrams. Some advice on how to prepare yourself for this kind of work is given on the next page.

III The U.K. Economy Here again there are two sections, multiple-choice questions and exercises.

(a) <u>Multiple-choice questions</u>. These are of the five-option type designed to test your knowledge of some basic features of the British economy.

(b) <u>Exercises</u>. These are of several different kinds, involving frequently the collection and presentation of data in tabular and graphical forms. Questions are posed which are designed to help you with practice in data-response techniques. You are asked to interpret data and to relate them to basic economic principles as well as, sometimes, to comment on their policy implications.

Detailed guidance on sources is given in most exercises calling for the collection of data. You should also refer to the reading guide on the next page. Some questions deal with very large numbers (thousands of millions of pounds, for example). You should realize that two, or at the most three, significant figures are quite enough for your purposes. Ignore all but the left-hand two or three digits by changing the others into zeros. You will also find it helpful in both graphs and tables to write 'millions', 'thousands', etc., on the axes or heads of columns to enable you to work with fewer digits.

A word of caution is necessary here. When doing exercises on the U.K. economy, remember that your results should always be treated with reserve. For example, you may be asked to consider whether or not a clear relationship exists between, for example, price and quantity or inflation and unemployment. The world is a complex place. It is virtually impossible, in practice, to hold constant some of the determinants of variables in which you are interested as can be done in theory with <u>ceteris paribus</u> assumptions. Apparent correlations between statistical series which move in association with each other may conceal profound and complex relationships. It is often dangerous to conclude that you have identified a <u>causal</u> relationship, i.e. that one variable <u>determines</u> another.

IV Essays Each chapter ends with a selection of essays. They are primarily intended to set you thinking about the implications of some piece of economic analysis. Quotations followed by the words 'comment' or 'discuss' are usually invitations to assess the validity of the statements, often also expecting you to make explicit the implicit assumptions which lie behind them. You might do well to think about several of the essay titles, even if you write on only one or two of them.

---

*I have recorded a set of audio tapes in which I explain why each incorrect answer is wrong. For details, please complete the form provided in the book or write to me at The City University, St John St, London EC1V 0PB.

The Use of Mathematics and Graphs in Economics

You will find that your ability to answer some of the questions in this workbook depends on an understanding of very elementary mathematics. The standard required does not extend beyond part of O-level.
One of the most common techniques is that of calculating percentages and proportions. It is also a
help in a few questions to know enough algebra to solve an equation with a single unknown, to understand the meaning of the slope of a curve and whether it shows a positive or negative relationship
between two variables. The maths are in all cases kept subsidiary to the economics and the amount of
arithmetical work kept to the absolute minimum.
        Diagrams are sometimes incorporated in questions. In other cases they may be implicit, but
deliberately not drawn. This is to give you practice in drawing them yourself and you may need to do
so in order to answer a question. Several of the exercises on the U.K. economy call for the prepara-
tion of graphs. You should refresh your memory on how to use and interpret them. It is sound advice
to use the largest graph paper available and to choose scales for the axes that take full advantage
of it.*

READING GUIDE

As previously stated, this workbook is not designed to accompany any particular text, but to be
suitable for use with those in common use. The list which follows is selective, but includes the
major British standard general textbooks at an introductory level as well as one or two of the best-
known American and a small number in special fields. Chapter numbers are given for each book to
correspond with the chapters in this workbook.

The U.K. economy Many of the best and most complete theory texts tend to be rather weak on the
descriptive and institutional side. There are, however, a few books which concentrate on these
aspects and which may therefore be particularly helpful for questions on the U.K. economy:

> Griffiths, A. and Wall Applied Economics (Longman, 1984)
> Harbury, C. Descriptive Economics (Pitman Books, 6th edn, 1981)
> Harbury, C. and Lipsey An Introduction to the UK Economy
>   (Weidenfeld and Nicolson, 1983)
> Maunder, P. (ed.) The British Economy in the 1970s (Heinemann, 1980)
> Morris, D. (ed.) The Economic System in the U.K. (Oxford University Press, 3rd edn, 1984)
> National Institute of Economic and Social Research, The United Kingdom Economy
>   (Heinemann, 4th edn, 1979)
> Prest, A. R. & Coppeck (eds) The U.K. Economy, A Manual of Applied Economics
>   (Weidenfeld & Nicolson, 10th edn, 1984)

You should, incidentally, always refer to the latest edition of these books, which tend to be
frequently revised to take account of changes that occur in the economy. Moreover, any book inevitably
dates more quickly than periodicals and it a good idea to try and develop the habit of referring to
sources such as:

> The Annual Abstract of Statistics
> The Monthly Digest of Statistics
> Economic Trends
> Britain, An Official Handbook

They are all published by Her Majesty's Stationery Office and are available in most public libraries.
They and others are cited for several exercises on the U.K. economy.

---

*An appendix on the use of graphs in economics appears in my Economic Behaviour : An Introduction
(Allen & Unwin, 1980).

	CHAPTER NUMBERS							
	1 The Subject Matter of Economics	2 Supply and Demand	3 Production: Costs and Organization	4 Distribution: Factors of Production and Their Prices	5 National Income	6 Money, Banking and the Price Level	7 Inter-national Trade	8 Economic Policy
Allport, J. A. & Stewart Economics (Cambridge University Press, 2nd edn, 1978)	1	15,16 20-2	14,19	17,18	2-4,11	4-9	9	8,13
Anderton, A. G. Economics, A New Approach (University Tutorial Press, 1984)	31	2,21-2	23-7	29-30	6,8,10-12 15,16	3-5, 13-14	17,18	9,19,28
Baumol, W. J. & Blinder Economics, Principles & Policy (Harcourt Brace, 2nd edn, 1982)	1,3	4,18-19	20-2, 24-7	32-3	6-10	12-17	37-9	13,15-17 23, 28-30, 34
Beardshaw, J. Economics: A Student's Guide (Macdonald and Evans, 1984)	1,3,6	8-12	13-18	4,20-4	7,28-32	33-6	37-40	19,25-7 41-4
Beckerman, W. An Introduction to National Income Analysis (Weidenfeld & Nicolson, 3rd edn, 1980)				7,8	1-6,9-12			
Begg, D. et al. Economics (British Edition) (McGraw Hill, 1984)	1,17	3-5	6-9	10-12	19-21	22-30	21,31-3	14-16,21
Black, J. The Economics of Modern Britain (Martin Robertson, 2nd edn, 1980)					1-10	12-14, 16-20	22-6	11,21, 27-8
Blight, D. and Shafto Introduction to Microeconomics (Pitman Books, 1984)	1	5-7	2-4,8-10	11				10
Brooman, F. S. Macroeconomics (Allen & Unwin, 6th edition, 1973)					1-7	10-13	8	
Burnett, D. et al. The Organization, Vols 2 and 3 (Sweet & Maxwell, 1979)	1(3)	1(3)	7(2),2(3)	1-6(2)			6(3)	7(3)
Burningham, D. (ed.) Understanding Economics (Macmillan, 1978)	1,2	5,6,8	3,4, 6,7	10	11-13	14-15	16-17	9,18
Cairncross, A. K. Economics (Butterworth, 6th edn, 1982)	1-3	10-13	13-16	3,18-20	21-2	23-6	27-9	30,31
Craven J. Introduction to Economics (Blackwell, 1984)	1,2	4,9	7,8,12,14	10	5,15,16	3,18	2,24-5	17,19-24 26
Creedy, J. Economics: An Integrated Approach (Prentice Hall, 1984)	1,2,6	4	6,11-15	16-19	3,22	21,23	28-30	8-10,20, 27,31
Edwards, G. J. The Framework of Economics (McGraw-Hill, 3rd edn, 1975)	1	9-12	4-8 13,14	2,3 17,18	15	19-22	23	24,25
Edwards, G. J. & Kellar The Organisation in its Environment (McGraw-Hill, Book I, 1979, Book II, 1980)		I(12-16)	I(3) II(6,7)	I(8-10)	II(2)	II(3)		II(1, 4,5)
Farquhar, J. D. The National Economy (Philip Allan, 1975)					1-6	7,8,12	6,11	8,13
Farquhar, J. D. & Heidenson The Market Economy (Philip Allan, 1975)		2	3					5
Fleming, M. Introduction to Economic Analysis (Allen & Unwin, 1969)	1-6	7,8 13,15	9-12 16-17	18-21	23-5	27-30	33-8	4,32
Ford, A. G. Income Spending and the Price Level (Fontana, 1971)					1-5	6-7	9	10
Gowland, D. H. (ed.) Modern Economic Analysis (Butterworths, 1979)						1		9-14
Grant, R. M. & Shaw (eds.) Current Issues in Economic Policy (Philip Allan, 2nd edn, 1980)			2,3	2			13	1,8,9
Griffiths, A. and Wall	1	9	3-8	18,21	11,12	2,15-17	22-24, 26,27	13,14, 19,25
Hanson, J. L. A Textbook of Economics (McDonald Evans, 7th edn, 1977)	1	9-12	2,6-8 13-15	3-5 17-19	16	20-5	26,7	28-30
Harbury, Colin Descriptive Economics (Pitman, 6th edn, 1981)	1	1	3-6	2,7	8	10	11	9
Harbury, Colin Economic Behaviour: An Introduction (Allen & Unwin, 1980)	1-3 11	4	4,5	5	6,7	8,9	2,6,9	9,10
Harbury C. & Lipsey Introduction to the UK Economy (Pitman, 1983)	1		2-3	4	7	8	5,7	6,9

	1 The Subject Matter of Economics	2 Supply and Demand	3 Production: Costs and Organization	4 Distribution: Factors of Production and Their Prices	5 National Income	6 Money, Banking and the Price Level	7 Inter-national Trade	8 Economic Policy
Hardwick P., et al. Introduction to Modern Economics (Longman, 1982)	1	3,4-6	2.9-10	15-16, 30	17,19-20	21-23,27	28-9	7-8,11-14, 18,26
Hartley, K. Problems of Economic Policy (Allen & Unwin, 1977)								1,8-10
Harvey, J. Basic Economics (Macmillan, 1981)	1,14	3,4,6	5-6	2,7-9	15,16	12,13	17	10,11, 18-21
Harvey, J. Intermediate Economics (Macmillan, 4th edn, 1983)	1	2,3	4-6	7-11	16-19	12-15	20-4	15,25
Harvey J. Elementary Economics Macmillan 5th edn 1982	1-2	8	4,5,9	7,16-18	19	10	20-1	6,22-5
Harvey, J. The Organisation in its Environment (Macmillan, 1980)	3	7,8	8-10	2,11	15,16	13,18	20	14,19
Harvey, J. & Johnson An Introduction to Macroeconomics (Macmillan, 1971)						8,9,15		11-14
Heertje, A. & Robinson Basic Economics (Holt Rinehart, 1979)	1,2	8	9-11	12	3,4	4-7	15	14
Hewitt, G. Economics of the Market (Fontana, 1974)	1	2-4	5,7-9	6				10-11
Hey, J. D. Britain in Context, (Blackwell, 1979)				43-52, 56-67	17-22		1-16	25-34, 68-74
Hocking, T. & Powell Investigating Economics (Longman, 1984)	1-4	5-7	8	9,10	15	11	12-13	14,16-24
King, D. T. & Hamilton Economics in Society (Allen & Unwin, 1976)		4	5					8-10
Lipsey, R. G. An Introduction to Positive Economics (Weidenfeld & Nicolson, 6th edn, 1983)	1-5	6-15	16-24	25-29	34-37	38-9	30-1	32-3, 43-5
Livesey, F. Economics (Polytech, rev edn, 1981)		3,6	2,4-6,9			8	15	10-14
Livesey, F. A Textbook of Economics (Polytech., 2nd edn, 1982)	1,2	22-3, 26	24	27	3-6,8	9,12	7	10,12, 20,28
Lobley, D. Success in Economics (Murray, 1974)	1	3,4 12	5-11, 13-15	6,21	22,22,27	16-19, 23,28	24-6	29
McArthur, A. G. & Loveridge Economic Theory and Organisation (McDonald Evans, 2nd edn, 1980)	1	6,12	2,3,5 7-11	13	14	15,16	19,20	12,18
McCormick, B. J. et al. Introducing Economics (Penguin, 3rd edn, 1983)	2,4	7-11	12,15-20	22-7	31-6	37,38,41	4,42-3	28-9,45
Manchester Economics Project (Ginn, 2nd edn, 1976)	1	1,5, 8,11	4,10, 11	3,9, 18	14-17, 19	6,12	7,13, 20	22
Marder, K. B. & Alderson Economic Society (Oxford University Press, 2nd edn, 1980)	1	8	4-7	2,3,9		10-12	14,15	13,16
Maunder, P. (ed.) The British Economy in the 1970s (Heinemann, 1980)				4,5		2	9-11	
Marshall, B. V. Comprehensive Economics (Longman, 2nd edn, 1975)		11	2-4, 10	1-10, 12	12	6,12	5	7
Morris, D. (ed.) The Economic System in the U.K. (Oxford University Press, 3rd edn, 1984)		2	3	13	4	11	6,15	8-14,24-6
National Institute of Social and Economic Research The United Kingdom Economy (Heinemann, 4th edn, 1979)			2	1,3	1	5	6	3,4,7
Nevin, E. T. A Textbook of Economic Analysis (Macmillan, 4th edn, 1976)	1,2	3-4,14	5-13	15-17	18, 25-6	20-4, 27	29-33	19,28
Nicholson, J. F. Modern British Economics (Allen & Unwin, 1973)		10	1,6,7	8		2	9	
Nobbs, J. Advanced Level Economics (McGraw-Hill, 3rd edn, 1983)	1,2	10	11-14	4-6	7	15-18	9	8,14

	1 The Subject Matter of Economics	2 Supply and Demand	3 Production: Costs and Organization	4 Distribution: Factors of Production and Their Prices	5 National Income	6 Money, Banking and the Price Level	7 International Trade	8 Economic Policy
				CHAPTER NUMBERS				
Pen, J. Modern Economics (Penguin, 2nd edn, 1980)					3,4	7-9	5	6,12
Perrow, J. A. Economics (University Tutorial Press, 3rd edn, 1977)		1,2,6	3-5,7	9-10,14	15,16	11-13	17-19	
Powicke, J. C. & May An Introduction to Economics (Edward Arnold, 3rd edn, 1977)	1	7-9	8	10	11	5	4,12	6, 14-16
Prest, A. R. & Coppock (eds) The U.K. Economy (Weidenfeld & Nicolson, 10th edn, 1984)			4	5	1	2	3	1,2
Samuelson, P. A. Economics (McGraw-Hill, 11th edn, 1980	1-3	4, 20-2	6, 23-6	27-31	10-14	15-19	33-6	8,9,19, 26,32,41
Sandford, C. T. The Economics of Public Finance (Pergamon, 2nd edn, 1978)								1-10
Sandford, C. T. Social Economics (Heinemann, 1977)		4			3			5-6, 9-16
Sapsford, D. & Ladd Essential Economics (Heinemann, 1977)	1-3	9-10	4-8,11		12	14	16	15
Shafto, T.A.C. Economics & Business Structure (Hulton, 1976)	1	6,8	2-9	11,12	10	13,14	17,18	15
Stanlake, G. F. Introductory Economics (Longman, 4th edn, 1983)	1,2	14	6-11 15,16	3-5,13, 18-21,36	17	22-5	26-9	12-16, 30-7
Stanlake, G. F. Macroeconomics: An Introduction (Longman, 3rd edn, 1984)					2-10	11-17	10,18	9,20
Stonier, A. W. & Hague A Textbook of Economic Theory (Longman, 5th edn, 1980)		1-3	5-9	10-15	19-21	18,22-4		24
Turvey, R. Demand and Supply (Allen & Unwin, 2nd edn, 1980)		1,6	4,5	3,7				
Ward, I. D. S. & Wright An Introduction to Market Capitalism (Longman Cheshire, 1977)	1-2	3-4	5,8,9					
West, W. H. The Organisation in the Environment (Thornes, 1979)	1	2	2,3	4	5	5	5	5

CHAPTER 1

The Subject Matter of Economics

Most introductory textbooks in economics begin by emphasizing the fact of SCARCITY as being central to a society's economic problems. A good or service must, it is said, be scarce before it can be of interest to economists. Scarcity is not, however, absolute. A good must be scarce in relation to the demand for it. Scarcity of goods and services arises from the fact that the RESOURCES available for production are limited, and therefore it is not possible to produce as much of all goods as everyone would like. There is, therefore, a problem of CHOICE in economics, of choosing how to allocate resources between competing uses. Economists distinguish between various groups of these resources, or FACTORS OF PRODUCTION, in ways which help their analysis. It is usual to regard them as falling into one of at least three broad groupings, LAND, LABOUR and CAPITAL. ENTERPRISE, the willingness to undertake the risks of production, is often considered as a fourth factor.

The notion of choice implies a central idea of economics — OPPORTUNITY COST — the real cost of producing a good in terms of the opportunity foregone of producing something else. The range of opportunities or possibilities open to a society is sometimes portrayed graphically as a PRODUCTION POSSIBILITY CURVE, also known as a TRANSFORMATION CURVE, or an OPPORTUNITY COST CURVE. Such a curve shows the various alternative combinations of goods which an economy can produce by fully utilizing the resources at its disposal. When production occurs at a point on the proudction possibility curve, resources are said to be allocated efficiently. The shape of the curve shows also how opportunity costs change as production increases. Such costs can be CONSTANT, INCREASING or DECREASING.

Economics is concerned with the allocation of resources between different uses, with the ways in which resources are combined to produce each good and with the distribution of goods among individuals. These matters are sometimes referred to as the central problems of an economy — what to produce, how to produce it and for whom the goods are produced. Such problems of resource allocation are the subject of what is called MICROECONOMICS. There is a second branch of the discipline, MACROECONOMICS, which is concerned with the behaviour of the economy as a whole and deals with such aggregates as the National Income, total employment and the general level of prices. When questions of resource alloca- tion are under consideration, it is common to ignore macroeconomic problems and to assume, for example, that all resources are fully employed.

Decisions on the economic problems of society can be taken in several ways. If they are made by a central authority, the economy is said to be CENTRALLY PLANNED or COMMAND. If production and distri- bution are the results of producers trying to make profits by selling goods at PRICES determined in MARKETS by the free interplay of SUPPLY AND DEMAND, the economy is said to be a MARKET ECONOMY, or one where the decisions are made through the PRICE MECHANISM. The term market in this connection merely implies that buyers and sellers are in touch with one another. Most societies at the present time have MIXED ECONOMIES, containing elements of both planning and the price mechanism. A few primitive societies remain outside this range. They are called SUBSISTENCE economies. In them, each unit produces all its own wants and does not exchange its products for those of other units.

Economists, as economists, cannot legitimately state a preference for one of the systems mentioned above, though as citizens they undoubtedly have personal views. A choice between them necessitates making VALUE JUDGEMENTS, which lie outside the scope of what is known as POSITIVE ECONOMICS. This deals with understanding how an economic system works — with such questions as the likely consequences of a change in the supply or demand for a good on production, consumption and market price. Positive statements in economics can be identified by the fact that they are testable, at least in principle, against the facts of the real world. In contrast, NORMATIVE economics deals with 'good' and 'bad' with what ought to be. Value judgements are involved and they should be explicitly stated as far as possible.

The task of positive economics is to arrange the determinants of economic events, such as price changes, in such a way that the outcome of changes in, say, supply or demand on market price can be estimated. Patterns of behaviour are studied and, where consistent patterns are found, so-called ECONOMIC LAWS are sometimes expounded. These are merely observed tendencies, which need not always apply to every single case. But PREDICTIONS of future events can at times be successfully made. They usually involve setting up a 'model' of the part of the economy under consideration. In the model the causal relationships between economic quantities such as supply, demand, price and income are specified. Models may be tested to see how well they fit the evidence of the real world. Because of the variability of the facts or data that economists have to work with, predictions are usuaully expressed in terms of PROBABILITIES. In this way economics lays some claim to being a SCIENCE though the normal methods of the physical sciences are not available to it. Instead of controlled repetitive laboratory experiments, economists usually engage in statistical analysis of past behaviour which often involves complex problems of interpretation. In so far as some of the determinants of economic events are not economic, economists may draw upon the work of other disciplines, especially the other SOCIAL SCIENCES, such as sociology, social psychology and political science.

ANALYSIS

Multiple Choice

Choose the alternative which provides the best answer to the question or completes the sentence most satisfactorily.

1 When economists refer to the existence of opportunity cost they mean that

   (a)   the cost of production of goods is measured in money terms.
   (b)   a good can never be produced without involving a sacrifice of not producing other goods.
   (c)   a country's resources are insufficient for the production of as much of any good that will completely satisfy total consumer requirements.
   (d)   all goods and services are in scarce supply.
   (e)   if resources are used for the production of any good they will not be available for the production of others.

2 Two years ago Fred Bates bought a new extending ladder to start up as a window-cleaner. Last week he fell and injured his back and decided to sell up and try a different kind of work. An economist advised him to value his equipment at its opportunity cost. What is the opportunity cost of the ladder to Fred now?

   (a)   The best price he can get by selling the ladder
   (b)   The original cost of the ladder
   (c)   The replacement cost of the ladder
   (d)   The cost of the ladder two years ago after allowing for inflation
   (e)   The value of the good he would have bought if he had not bought the ladder

3 All but one of the following involve an economic problem. Which is the one that does not?

   (a)   How long it took Agatha Christie to write 'Murder on the Orient Express'.
   (b)   How long it takes to play Chopin's Minute Waltz.
   (c)   How many pictures were painted by Picasso.
   (d)   How Charlie Chaplin would have earned his living if he had not been a film actor.
   (e)   How many people want to see a production of 'Macbeth' at the National Theatre.

4 Which of the following are considered factors of production?

   1.   Machinery
   2.   Consumer goods
   3.   Land and free gifts of nature
   4.   Unskilled labour
   5.   Risk-taking business men

   (a)   1 and 3 only
   (b)   2,4 and 5 only
   (c)   1,4 and 5 only
   (d)   1,3,4 and 5 only
   (e)   1,2,3,4 and 5

5 Which of the following is most likely to lead to an increase in the supply of skilled labour?

   (a)   A fall in the death rate
   (b)   A rise in the emigration rate
   (c)   A raising of the school-leaving age
   (d)   A fall in the birth rate
   (e)   A fall in the general level of unemployment

6 Which of the following is essential for the existence of a market economy?

(a) Prices
(b) Banks
(c) Trade unions
(d) Economists
(e) Economic laws

7 The distinctive features of a market economy are that

(a) all goods and services are bought for money.
(b) the government takes charge of marketing arrangements for particular commodities.
(c) resources are allocated by the price mechanism.
(d) market prices tend to rise with inflation.
(e) buyers and sellers meet face to face in markets.

8 In a mixed economy in peacetime which of the following features are usually present?

1. Central planning of some production
2. Free market determination of prices of some goods and services
3. The government raises some income by taxation
4. Labour is directed to work in different industries
5. Businesses strive to make profits

(a) 2 only
(b) 2 and 5 only
(c) 1,3 and 4 only
(d) 1,2,3 and 5 only
(e) 1,2,3,4 and 5

9 Which of the following is a microeconomic problem?

(a) The rate of inflation
(b) The value of total imports
(c) The rate of economic growth
(d) The level of efficiency in the coal industry
(e) The level of total unemployment

10 Which of the following is a macroeconomic problem?

(a) The price of houses
(b) The value of exports of machinery
(c) The wages of skilled workers
(d) The quantity of wheat produced
(e) The level of total investment

11 Economists tend to make rather less accurate predictions than some physical scientists because

(a) people do not always behave as consistently as inanimate objects.
(b) controlled experiments are virtually impossible in the social sciences.
(c) economic events frequently have very complicated causes.
(d) non-economic factors also influence economic events.
(e) All of the above are reasons why economists are not able to make as accurate predictions as some physical scientists.

12 Positive statements in economics are

(a) assertions concerning economic policy which involve value judgements.
(b) observations concerning economic events which can usually be accurately forecast.
(c) factual statements or predictions about the behaviour of an economy which can, in principle, be tested.
(d) observations concerning past events which are known with positive certainty.
(e) statements about particular kinds of economic forces which are positively associated with each other.

13 Which of the following statements is normative rather than positive?

(a) An increase in advertising expenditure should raise sales.
(b) The rate of unemployment should be lower.
(c) Nationalization of oil companies will lower costs of production.
(d) A rise in income tax rates will lower work incentives.
(e) Inflation stimulates investment.

14 A production possibility curve for two goods (apricots and biscuits) portrays

   (a) all alternative efficient combinations of biscuits and apricots which an economy is capable
        of producing.
   (b) all the combinations of biscuits and apricots that the economy has produced over a given,
        stated, period of time in the past.
   (c) the maximum quantity of apricots which can be produced if no biscuits are produced.
   (d) the cost of producing both biscuits and apricots in money terms.
   (e) the alternative ways open to society of producing a given quantity of biscuits and apricots.

15 If the production possibility curve for two goods shifts so that it moves further from the origin
       throughout its length this could be due to

   (a) an increase in the productivity of all factors of production.
   (b) an increase in the level of unemployment.
   (c) an increase in consumers' demand for both goods.
   (d) the fact that the costs of one good decrease as more is produced.
   (e) a reduction in productivity of all factors of production.

16 With reference to Fig. 1.1, which of the following statements is correct?

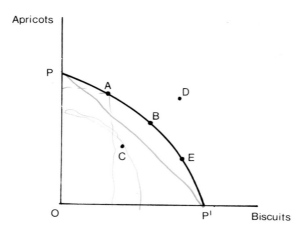

Fig. 1.1

   (a) If the economy is at point C there must be heavy unemployment.
   (b) Neither point C nor point D represents attainable production possibilities.
   (c) If the economy is at point D, some factors of production are being used inefficiently.
   (d) At point A the economy would be producing less biscuits and more apricots than at E.
   (e) If the economy is at point P it shows that the cost of producing biscuits is so high that
        none can be produced.

17 Which of the following suggests that the production possibility curve will be a straight line
       (not a true curve)?

   (a) The economy is at full employment.
   (b) All factors of production receive equal incomes.
   (c) The costs of producing one good in terms of the other are constant.
   (d) Diminishing returns apply to all factors of production.
   (e) The scales used on the graph are linear.

Problems

1 In Fig. 1.2 the curve AA' represents the current production possibility curve per month for an economy producing apricots and biscuits. In each one of the following situations which would be the most likely production on possibility curve for the same economy?

  (i)   There is a fall in productivity in apricot production.
  (ii)   There is large-scale emigration.
  (iii) The cost of producing apricots in terms of biscuits rises.
  (iv)   There is heavy unemployment.
  (v)   The public suddenly start to like biscuits more and apricots less.
  (vi)   New machinery raises productivity in labour generally.

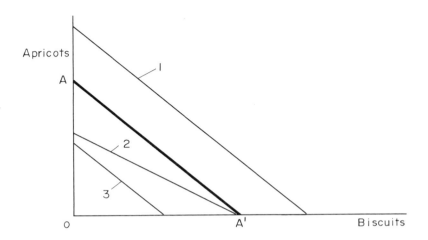

Fig. 1.2

2 The economy of Mythica can produce only two goods, apples and bananas. The following table shows some of the combinations of the two goods that can be produced per week when all of its resources are fully employed in the most efficient manner.

Apples	20	18	14	10	4	0
Bananas	0	2	5	7	9	10

Plot the six points on graph paper and join them up in a smooth curve to represent Mythica's production possibility curve.

  (i)   As apple production is increased what happens to costs of production of apples in terms of bananas?
  (ii)   As banana production is increased, what happens to costs of production of bananas in terms of apples?
  (iii) As banana production is increased, what happens to costs of production of apples in terms of bananas?
  (iv)   If Mythica is producing 6 bananas, what is the maximum number of apples that can be produced?
  (v)   Assume that cost conditions change and that Mythica can now produce the following combinations: 20 apples and no bananas, 10 apples and 5 bananas, or 10 bananas and no apples. Draw the new production possibility curve.

  (a) Are costs of production increasing, decreasing or constant?
  (b) If the economy is producing 6 apples, what is the maximum number of bananas it can produce?

3 The five curves in Fig. 1.3 show various production possibility curves for an economy producing combs and brushes. Which curve (or curves) would apply in the following circumstances?

A BC (i) The cost of producing brushes in terms of combs is constant as more brushes are produced.
E (ii) The cost of producing brushes in terms of combs rises as more brushes are produced.
(iii) The cost of producing brushes in terms of combs falls as fewer brushes are produced.
(iv) The cost of producing combs in terms of brushes falls as more combs are produced.
(v) The cost of producing combs in terms of brushes falls as more brushes are produced.

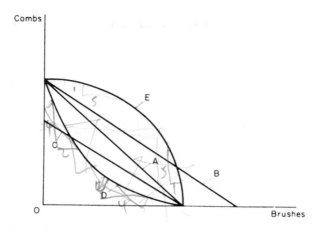

Fig. 1.3

U.K. ECONOMY

Multiple Choice

Choose the alternative which provides the best answer to the question or completes the sentence most satisfactorily.

1 The population of the U.K. in 1981 was approximately

    (a)   13 million
    (b)   24 million
    (c)   35 million
    (d)   45 million
    (e)   56 million

2 The density of population is the number of persons per square mile. Select from the following figures the approximate density for

    (i) England (ii) Scotland (iii) Wales (iv) Northern Ireland

    (a)   60
    (b)   175
    (c)   300
    (d)   350
    (e)   900

3 Approximately what percentage of the total U.K. population is the 'working population'?

    (a)   35%
    (b)   45%
    (c)   55%
    (d)   65%
    (e)   75%

4 Which of the following regions of the U.K. has had (i) the largest and (ii) the smallest relative
increase in total population since the beginning of the present century?

(a) Midlands
(b) Northern England
(c) Wales
(d) Scotland
(e) Northern Ireland

5 Which of the following categories contains (i) the largest and (ii) the smallest number of persons?

(a) Farm workers
(b) Clerks
(c) Factory workers
(d) Transport workers
(e) Professional workers

6 Which of the following categories contains (i) the largest and (ii) the smallest number of persons?

(a) Agriculture
(b) Distribution
(c) Government
(d) Manufacturing
(e) Transport

7 Which of the following has increased most in supply in the U.K. since the Second World War?

(a) Land
(b) Labour
(c) Capital
(d) Coal
(e) All have increased by about the same amount.

8 Of the total land in Britain (i) the largest and (ii) the smallest area is

(a) used for growing tillage crops.
(b) grazing and grassland.
(c) inland water.
(d) forest.
(e) urban.

9 What proportion of total output of goods and services in the U.K. is accounted for by (i) secondary
and (ii) tertiary production?

(a) 15%
(b) 25%
(c) 40%
(d) 55%
(e) 75%

10 Which of the following British industries produces (i) the largest and (ii) the smallest total
output?

(a) Food, drink and tobacco
(b) Clothing
(c) Coal
(d) Chemicals
(e) Engineering

11 Which of the following British industries expanded (i) the most and (ii) the least during the
1970s?

(a) Chemicals
(b) Vehicles
(c) Food, drink and tobacco
(d) Textiles
(e) Shipbuilding

12 With one exception the following are ways in which the government tries to influence the allocation of resources in peacetime in Britain. Which is the exception?

(a) Imposing taxes and granting subsidies
(b) Directing labour to move from regions of relatively low to those of relatively high unemployment
(c) Acquiring and running industries
(d) Prohibiting certain kinds of production
(e) Directly controlling prices

Exercises

Note: Sources are suggested for all exercises. Alternatives may be available if the one mentioned is not in your library. For advice on them and on the collection and presentation of data in tabular and graphical form see pp.ix-x.

1 Complete the following table showing the Gross Domestic Product of each of the listed sectors for the latest year available and another 5-10 years ago. Calculate the percentage of the total in each case.

	Year 19....		Year 19....	
	£m	%	£m	%
Agriculture, forestry and fishing				
Mining and quarrying				
Manufacturing				
Construction				
Transport and communication				
Distributive trades				
Insurance, banking, finance, etc.				
Others				
Totals		100%		100%

Source: Annual Abstract of Statistics

(i)   Which sectors are mainly primary, secondary and tertiary in nature?
(ii)   Which sectors have exhibited relative expansion or contraction between the two dates?
(iii) If sectors have changed their relative importance in the totals for the economy, can you say whether this was because of changing demand or changing costs of production? Are there any other explanations to be offered?

2 Construct a graph showing the course of production in the following manufacturing industries (as indicated by the Index of Industrial Production) for each of the last five years.

Engineering
Textiles
Vehicles
Chemicals
All manufacturing (Source: Annual Abstract of Statistics)

(i)   Comment on the trends shown in the graph and suggest any likely causes.
(ii)   Are the trends of the last five years similar to or different from those over a longer period?
(iii) Do you expect the trends shown in the graph to continue in the future? Why or why not?

3 Complete the following table showing the size of the total population and the 'dependant population' for each of the Census years of the present century. Count as dependants those below school-leaving age and above the age of retirement.

| Year | Population | | | | % Dependent |
	Total (i)	In education (ii)	Dependent Retired (iii)	All (iv)	$\frac{(iv)}{(i)} \times 100$ (v)
1901					
1911					
1921					
1931					
1951					
1961					
1971					
1981					

Source: Annual Abstract of Statistics

(i) How has the size of the dependent population changed relative to the total?

(ii) Is the change in (i) above due more to alterations in the relative size of the younger or older age groups?

(iii) Are the trends likely to continue for the remainder of the century? How confident can one be about this?

4 Find out the total employment in each of the following industries for a recent year and another ten years previously. Then obtain measures of the volume of output for the same industries for the same years. (Use figures of physical output or of the value of output at constant prices.)

    Agriculture
    Coal
    Motor vehicles
    Iron and steel
    Road passenger transport
    (Source: Annual Abstract of Statistics)

(i) Calculate the average output per worker in each of the two years.

(ii) Compute the change in labour productivity between the two years.

(iii) Suggest reasons for any differences in productivity change you found in (ii) above?

(iv) If you had figures for the capital used in each industry as well as labour, what differences in productivity would you expect to find?

5 Complete the following table showing the total numbers of workers, the numbers unemployed and the percentage rates of unemployment in the regions shown for the latest year available and another 5-10 years ago.

| | Year 19.... | | | Year 19.... | | |
	Numbers Unemployed	Total	% Unemployed	Numbers Unemployed	Total	% Unemployed
South East						
West Midlands						
North						
North West						
Scotland						
Wales						
U.K.						

Source: Annual Abstract of Statistics

(i) Which regions had the highest and lowest unemployment rates in each year?

(ii) Which regions had the largest and the smallest change in unemployment rates between the two years?

(iii) What explanations can you offer for your findings in (i) and (ii) above?

(iv) How similar or different are your findings to the experiences of the 1930s and to those of early post-war years?

6 Collect figures of (i) the real value of the Gross Domestic Product (i.e. GDP at constant prices) and (ii) the total population for each of the last ten years. (Source: <u>Annual Abstract of Statistics</u>.) Divide (i) by (ii) to give estimates of output <u>per capita</u>. Plot the series on a graph.

  (i) Can you tell from the slope of the line you plotted which years showed the greatest and the smallest change in output per capita?

 (ii) How far does the graph help you understand what happened to living standards over the period?

(iii) What additional information would you need to estimate the change in productivity between the first and last years?

7 Obtain figures for a recent year of the total income and the total numbers of incomes before tax in each size class given in the following table. Calculate the percentages of the totals in columns (ii) and (iv).

Range of income before tax	Total income		Numbers of incomes	
	£m (i)	% (ii)	Thousands (iii)	% (iv)
Less than £2000				
£2000 to £4999				
£5000 to £9999				
£10 000 to £19 999				
£20 000 and over				
Totals		100%		100%

<u>Source</u>: Annual Abstract of Statistics

  (i) What percentages of total income would those in the first and last rows in the table have to receive if incomes were equally distributed between these two groups?

 (ii) Compare the actual figures in the table with those you offered in answer to (i) above. Do the differences give any idea of the degree of inequality in income distribution?

(iii) What are the major reasons for the inequality shown by the table?

 (iv) What measures are taken by the government to reduce the degree of inequality in income distribution?

8 For the most recent year for which you can find statistics and another five or more years earlier, find out the total turnover of the following types of retail business:

        Single outlet retailers
        Small multiple retailers
        Large multiple retailers
        Co-operative societies
        (Source: <u>Annual Abstract of Statistics</u>)

Calculate the shares of total retail business accounted for by each category in the two years.

  (i) Which category has the largest and the smallest share in each year?

 (ii) Which category increased or reduced its share relatively most between the two years?

(iii) What reasons can you suggest for the trends in (ii) above?

 (iv) If you had used figures of the numbers of outlets rather than those of turnover, what differences would you expect to have found?

9 Obtain figures of the value of exports and imports of the U.K. in each of the categories in the following table for a recent year and another ten years previously. Calculate the percentages of the total value of exports and imports in every case.

	Year 19....		Year 19....	
	£m	%	£m	%
Food, beverages and tobacco				
Crude materials				
Mineral fuels and oils				
Chemicals				
Manufactured goods				
Machinery and transport equipt.				
Other				
Totals		100%		100%

Source: Annual Abstract of Statistics

(i) Describe in words the changes that have taken place in the structure of import and export trade over the period?

(ii) How dependent on the rest of the world is the U.K. for its foodstuffs?

(iii) How does the structure of British foreign trade in recent years differ from the pattern before the First World War?

10 Find the total expenditure of the government (central and local) and the total national income for a recent year and another ten years previously. (Source: Annual Abstract of Statistics.) Express government expenditure as percentages of national income in the two years.

(i) What explanations can you suggest for any change that may have occurred between the two years?

(ii) What are the main ways in which the government finances its expenditure?

(iii) How far is it true to say that the figure for total government expenditure represents a public claim on resources decided in Whitehall?

Essays

1. What economic problems are faced by a family?

2. Using examples to illustrate your answer distinguish between real opportunity costs and historical accounting costs.

3. What is meant by describing economics as the 'science of choice'? To what extent do you consider it is a satisfactory definition?

4. Distinguish between the major factors of production, land, labour, capital and enterprise.

5. Explain carefully the difference between goods, services and factors of production.

6. How do changes in birth- and death-rates affect the size of (a) the total population and (b) the working population of a country?

7. On what does the size of a country's dependent population depend?

8. Why can it be said that capital goods have no direct value in themselves but indirect value in the future?

9. Is education a consumer good, a capital good or both?

10. What are the functions of prices in a market economy?

11. What did Adam Smith mean when he wrote about the 'invisible hand'?

12. What is a 'mixed economy'?

13. Explain why the statement that 'the rate of inflation is too high in Britain' is a normative one. Suggest a reformulation to turn it into a positive statement and consider how it might then be tested.

14. To what extent do you believe that economists can make policy recommendations without at the same time making value judgements?

15. What is the difference between microeconomics and macroeconomics?

16. What is meant by putting an economic theory to the test?

17. Why may it be said that economics uses 'scientific methods'?

18. If two economic variables always move up and down together does this mean that one <u>causes</u> the other? Give examples to illustrate your answer.

19. What is measured by the slope of a production possibility curve. How and why can it vary?

20. Explain the difference between the following changes: (a) those involving a movement <u>of</u> a production possibly curve, (b) those involving a movement <u>on to</u> a production possibility curve, and (c) those involving a movement <u>along</u> a production possibility curve.

21. What is a production possibility curve? If it is concave to (i.e. 'bulges out from') the origin, what does this imply about underlying opportunity costs?

CHAPTER 2

Supply and Demand

The work of this chapter is devoted to questions of resource allocation in the market for a single commodity.

Resource allocation by the price mechanism is analysed with the use of the concepts of SUPPLY and DEMAND. In a market economy, resources are directed to the production of different goods by movements in their relative prices. If people want to purchase a good and price covers the cost of production, it is assumed that businesses will engage in its production in order to make a profit.

If the price of a good is such that the amount which consumers wish to buy is not the same as the amount which suppliers are prepared to offer for sale, there will be some pressure on its price. If, on the other hand, price is such as to clear the market exactly with no disappointed consumers or producers, then the price and the market are said to be in EQUILIBRIUM. If price is above equilibrium there is excess supply of the good and producers will tend to compete with each other by lowering price. If the price is below equilibrium there is excess demand and some consumers will be prepared to pay more for the good, which will tend to push the price up. In such cases equilibrium is said to be stable, in that deviations from equilibrium set up economic forces which restore equilibrium. In some cases, e.g. when there are time lags between price and quantity changes, equilibrium may be unstable, when divergencies from equilibrium are not self-restoring. However, when a change occurs in the conditions of either supply or demand, such a reduction in costs or a shift in tastes, in so far as it exerts pressure on the price of a good, it will normally set up market forces leading towards a new equilibrium.

The forces of supply and demand working through the price mechanism can be thought of as helping to solve the central economic problems of any society. Prices act, as it were, as signals which perform two functions. (i) Prices signal to suppliers the demand for different goods and services. Comparing prices with costs, producers can decide how to allocate resources in order to maximise profits. (ii) Prices signal to buyers the costs of acquiring different goods and services. Comparing prices with the satisfaction that goods bring, buyers can decide how to allocate their expenditure in order to maximize their satisfaction. In changing circumstances, prices act as signals to producers to adjust the allocation of resources. Prices also function to ration a limited supply among those who are prepared to pay most for it.

The DEMAND for a commodity is generally thought of as being by 'consumers' (or 'households'). It is rarely for a fixed amount, but is considered as a SCHEDULE of quantities which would be bought in the course of a given period of time at various prices. It is sometimes referred to specifically as the schedule of EFFECTIVE DEMAND to emphasize that it is not mere desires which are relevant but wants backed by preparedness to buy. The relationship between demand and price may be portrayed graphically as a DEMAND CURVE, with price plotted on the vertical axis and the quantity demanded on the horizontal axis. Market demand is made up of the demands of all individual consumers, and there is an observed tendency for demand curves to slope downwards to the right. This may be explained in two ways. First, as price falls, the number of persons entering the market as purchasers tends to increase. Second, as price falls, there is a tendency for each individual consumer to demand more. The second reason is related to the principle of DIMINISHING MARGINAL UTILITY.

Consumers are considered to derive satisfaction (or utility) from a good, though it is not pretended that this may be precisely measured. As their consumption of the good in a given period of time rises, the extra or MARGINAL UTILITY realized from consuming an additional unit of it tends to fall. A drop in price is in a sense, therefore, necessary to induce additional consumption. The principle just referred to rests upon the assumption of ceteris paribus (other things remaining equal). Moreover, a demand curve itself is drawn upon ceteris paribus assumptions (the CONDITIONS OF DEMAND) that all influences upon demand other than price are unchanged. For the quantity demanded is determined not by price alone but by many additional factors. The most important 'other' influences are the prices of other goods (which may be substitutes or complements), expectations about future prices, incomes (both size and distribution), the population, weather, tastes, etc., which may be important in particular cases. These influences are assumed to be held constant when a demand curve is constructed in order to allow for the separate consideration of each of them. When any one (or more) such influence changes there is a shift of the whole demand curve. This must be distinguished from movements along the curve — sometimes known as EXTENSIONS or CONTRACTIONS of demand, which refer to changes in demand _induced_ by changes in price.

A consumer is assumed to try to allocate his income in such a way as to maximize his satisfaction, at which point he is said to be in _equilibrium_. This occurs when the marginal utility (in money terms) of a good to the consumer is equal to its price. When two goods are being considered together, the condition for equilibrium is that the ratio of the prices of the two goods shall equal the ratio of their marginal utilities (alternatively that the ratio of the marginal utility of each good to its price is equal to the ratio of the marginal utility of each other good to _its_ price). This does not imply that the total utilities derived from each and every good are equal, since there is no reason to suppose that the utility derived from all goods declines at the same rate. It simply says that the last unit of money spent provides the consumer with the same satisfaction irrespective of the good on which it is spent. The difference between total utility (in money terms) of a commodity and the total outlay on it by a consumer, however, has significance in economics, and is a measure of what is known as CONSUMER SURPLUS.

Consumer behaviour is sometimes analysed with the use of INDIFFERENCE CURVES. Each indifference curve portrays all _combinations_ of two goods which provide the consumer with a given level of satisfaction. An individual is assumed to have a set of indifference curves, each representing a different level of total satisfaction. A BUDGET LINE, or PRICE RATIO LINE, the slope of which is given by the relative prices of two goods, is superimposed on the consumer's indifference map and represents the possibilities open to him, given his income, of buying two commodities. The consumer's equilibrium position is found at the point where the budget line is tangential to the highest attainable indifference curve. At this point the ratio of prices of the goods is equal to the ratio of their marginal utilities, or the MARGINAL RATE OF SUBSTITUTION between them. The latter is the rate at which an individual is prepared to exchange one good for another without being either better off or worse off. It is measured by the _slope_ of the indifference curve, and is found by drawing a tangent to it.

Indifference curve analysis may be used to show that the effect of a change in price can be regarded as being partly an INCOME EFFECT and partly a SUBSTITUTION EFFECT. The income effect abstracts from the change in _relative prices_ and arises from the changed _purchasing power_ (or _real income_) felt by a consumer with a fixed _money_ income, when price changes. It can be either positive or negative, i.e. a rise in income leading to an increase or decrease in demand for a good respectively. In the latter case the good in question is termed INFERIOR. The substitution effect of a price change is simply the effect of the change in _relative prices_, real income remaining constant. It can never be negative, i.e. a fall in price cannot, through the substitution effect, cause a fall in the quantity demanded (nor a rise in price a rise in quantity). For normal goods the income and substitution effects work in the same direction. In the case of an inferior good, the substitution effect is usually expected to more than offset the income effect, so that demand curves normally slope downwards. Where this is not the case the good is described as a 'Giffen good'.

The SUPPLY of a commodity is, like demand, related to a number of different factors. The SUPPLY SCHEDULE and SUPPLY CURVE show the amounts of a commodity which potential sellers, referred to variously as PRODUCERS, BUSINESSES, FIRMS or SUPPLIERS, are prepared to offer for sale at different prices during a given period of time. Supply curves often tend to slope upwards, i.e. sellers offer larger amounts for sale at high prices than at low ones. Supply, however, is strongly affected by costs of production, the state of technology, the form of business organization and the type of market in which the firm is operating. These may be called CONDITIONS OF SUPPLY, and are dealt with in the next chapter.

The responsiveness of demand and supply to price changes differs from one commodity to another. The measure of responsiveness used by economists is known as the coefficient of ELASTICITY, defined as the percentage (or proportionate) change in quantity divided by the determining percentage (or proportionate) change in price. The numerical value of this ratio normally varies between zero and infinity.

It is useful to distinguish three limiting cases of elasticity with the values of 0, 1 and infinity. Where the ELASTICITY OF DEMAND equals 1 (or unity), the percentage changes in price and quantity are the same; a rise or fall in price does not affect total revenue (price times quantity) or the receipts of the seller. When the value exceeds unity, demand is said to be elastic; a change in price changes total revenue in the opposite direction to the change in price. When the value is infinity, demand is said to be _perfectly elastic_; a change in price calls forth an infinitely large increase or decrease in the quantity demanded. When the value is less than unity, demand is said to be relatively inelastic; a change in price alters total revenue in the same direction as the change in price. When the value is zero, demand is _perfectly inelastic_; a change in price does not affect the quantity demanded at all. Graphically, a perfectly elastic demand curve is a horizontal straight line; a perfectly inelastic curve is vertical. A demand curve with unit elasticity at all points is a rectangular hyperbola. The sign of the coefficient of elasticity of demand is technically negative because price and quantity demanded usually vary inversely with each other, but this is conventionally ignored as a rule, i.e. a demand curve with elasticity equal to -1 is referred to as being equal to unity.

The elasticity of a supply curve is also usually distinguished by three similar limiting cases. The main difference is that price and quantity move in the same direction with an upward-sloping supply curve (i.e. its sign is positive). Total revenue, therefore, increases for a rise in price (and vice versa). Graphically, perfectly elastic and inelastic supply curves have the same shape as the corresponding demand curves. Unit elastic supply curves, however, are straight lines which, if projected, would pass through the origin. Relatively elastic and inelastic straight-line supply curves cut the price and the quantity axes respectively.

Elasticity of supply or demand measures responsiveness at a particular price, or point, on a curve. Except for horizontal and vertical curves, elasticity varies at different points along a straight-line demand curve. In the case of non-linear curves (i.e. curves which are not straight lines) tangents are drawn to the curve to estimate elasticity, though the slope alone does <u>not</u> measure elasticity in the general case.

The principal determinant of elasticity is the <u>availability of substitutes</u>. In the case of demand, this means mainly the number and closeness of susbtitute goods open to the consumer. Elasticity is also affected by the number of uses to which a good may be put and the proportion of income devoted to it. In practice the time allowed for a change in price to take effect is also important. In the case of supply, elasticity depends chiefly on the degree of substitutability between factors of production. This, too, is liable to be influenced by the time allowed for a change in price to take effect.

The elasticity of demand and supply discussed above is more precisely the (point) <u>PRICE elasticity</u> and it refers to very small price changes. Other elasticities are used in different cases. <u>ARC elasticity</u> is an <u>average</u> measure of elasticity where large price changes are involved. <u>CROSS</u> elasticity of demand is a measure of the responsiveness of the demand for one good to a change in the price of another. <u>INCOME elasticity of demand</u> is the responsiveness of demand for a good to a change in income.

Changes in supply and demand are often analysed using the measure of elasticity and a distinction is frequently drawn between SHORT-RUN and LONG-RUN effects. Momentary (or immediate), even shorter than short-run, effects may also be considered. Certain common reactions of demand and supply to price changes are sometimes known as 'LAWS' of supply and demand, e.g. that a fall in demand tends to lead to a lower price and to a reduction in the quantity sold. Such 'laws' are no more than tendencies, logically deduced, which are no truer than the assumptions — <u>ceteris paribus</u> included — on which they are based (and the curves themselves drawn). They are not <u>factual statements</u>, but hypotheses. Their validity should be tested against the facts of the real world.

ANALYSIS

Multiple Choice

Choose the alternative which provides the best answer to the question or completes the sentence most satisfactorily.

1 An individual's demand for a good is liable to be influenced by all but one of the following. Which is the exception?

(a) The price of the good
(b) The prices of other substitute goods
(c) The prices of other complementary goods
(d) The state of technology
(e) The individual's tastes

2 A firm's supply curve for a good is liable to be influenced by all but one of the following. Which is the exception?

(a) The productivity of factors of production
(b) The firm's goals
(c) The demand for the good
(d) The state of technology
(e) The costs of production

3

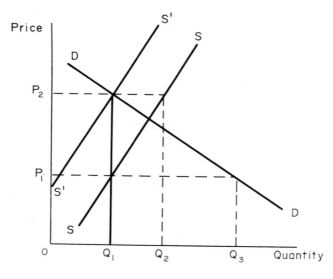

Fig. 2.1

Fig. 2.1 shows the supply and demand curves for eggs. The market is in equilibrium until disease reduces supply to S'S'. Which of the following statements is correct?

1. There is excess supply compared with the old equilibrium of Q_1Q_2.
2. There is excess demand compared with the old equilibrium of Q_1Q_3.
3. The new equilibrium price is OP_2.
4. Price rises by P_1P_2.
5. Quantity supplied falls by Q_1Q_2.

(a) 3 only
(b) 1 and 2 only
(c) 4 and 5 only
(d) 1,2,4 and 5 only
(e) 1,2,3,4 and 5

4 Which of the following provides the strongest evidence that a market is in equilibrium?

(a) The quantity bought is equal to the quantity sold.
(b) Stocks in the hands of producers are being run down.
(c) Prices are identical for all firms.
(d) Waiting lists are falling.
(e) Unfilled orders are zero.

5 The so-called Paradox of Value is sometimes illustrated by the fact that the price of water is lower than the price of champagne. This example assumes that the

(a) total utility of water is greater than the total utility of champagne.
(b) marginal utility of water is greater than the marginal utility of champagne.
(c) total utility of water is equal to the total utility of champagne.
(d) marginal utility of water is equal to the marginal utility of champagne.
(e) marginal utility of water is greater than the total utility of water.

6 The table below lists the quantities of toothbrushes supplied and demanded at a range of prices in a market. All but one of the following statements are correct. Which is the _incorrect_ statement?

Price (pence)	Quantities supplied	Quantities demanded
40	20	110
45	40	100
50	60	90
55	80	80
60	100	70

(a) The equilibrium market price is 55p.
(b) At a market price of 60p, excess demand is negative.
(c) If the quantities both supplied and demanded rise by 50% at every price, the equilibrium quantity will be 120.
(d) If the quantities demanded fall by 50% at every price while supply remains unchanged, the equilibrium quantity will be 40.
(e) If the quantities supplied increase by 25% while those demanded are halved the equilibrium market price will be 45p.

7 A reason for holding 'other things constant' (<u>ceteris paribus</u>) in supply-demand analysis is

(a) to facilitate the analysis of a number of independent influences on the market price of a good.
(b) to justify the use of value judgments in supply and demand analysis.
(c) to allow for the effects of changes in supply on a demand curve and vice versa.
(d) to avoid confusing the cause and effect of one variable on another in price determination.
(e) to examine the effects of 'other factors' on the market price of a good.

8 Which of the following could explain why the demand curve for a particular product slopes down from left to right?

(a) Incomes fall at the same time as price.
(b) Costs of production fall as output increases.
(c) The population is increasing.
(d) More consumers are willing to buy at low prices than at high.
(e) Total utility falls as consumption increases.

9 Which of the following could cause (i) a shift to the left of demand curve and (ii) a downward movement along a demand curve?

(a) A fall in the price of a complementary good
(b) A fall in the price of a substitute good
(c) A fall in the price of the good itself
(d) An increase in the number of consumers in the market
(e) An increase in costs of production

10 The assumption of diminishing marginal utility implies that

(a) the more one has of a commodity the less one values the first units bought.
(b) the satisfaction derived from a commodity falls the longer the period of time allowed.
(c) the total utility derived from consumption of a good changes less with increasing quantities of it.
(d) the price of a commodity tends to decline the greater the quantity supplied.
(e) the quantity of a good purchased tends to fall the more other influences than price are allowed to affect demand.

11 Which of the following could explain why the supply curve for a commodity slopes downwards?

(a) Producers do not like increasing production.
(b) Producers have to lower price to induce consumers to buy more.
(c) Costs fall as production increases.
(d) Diminishing marginal utility is in operation.
(e) The elasticity of supply is equal to zero.

12 Which of the following could cause an upward and leftward movement of an upward-sloping supply curve for a commodity?

(a) The imposition of an excise tax
(b) A rise in productivity
(c) A fall in production costs
(d) A rise in the supply of labour
(e) A shift of tastes in favour of the product

13 The supply curve for a commodity is assumed to slope upwards from left to right. Which of the following would cause it to shift downwards to the right?

(a) An increase in consumers' income
(b) A rise in the price of a substitute
(c) A unit subsidy from the government
(d) An excise tax imposed by the government
(e) Technological change raising costs of production

14 The supply schedule for a commodity is usually assumed to be directly open to influence by all the following <u>except</u>

(a) the quantity demanded.
(b) the prices of the factors of production.
(c) the costs of production.
(d) the number of firms in the industry.
(e) technological change.

15

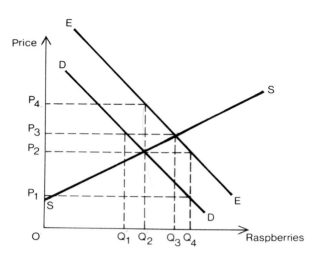

Fig. 2.2

Fig. 2.2 shows an increase in demand following a change in consumers' tastes in favour of raspberries. This will be likely to lead to

(a)   an increase in the quantity bought from OQ_2 to OQ_4 in the long run.
(b)   a rise in price from OP_2 to OP_4 in the very short run.
(c)   a new equilibrium price of OP_2 and equilibrium quantity of OQ_2.
(d)   a rise in price from OP_1 to OP_3 and an increase in quantity bought and sold from OQ_1 to OQ_3.
(e)   none of the above because the supply curve will shift to the right when price rises.

16 The market for a commodity is said to be in equilibrium when

(a)   the amount bought equals the amount sold.
(b)   price is such that consumers do not wish to buy more.
(c)   the quantity offered for sale is such that producers are exactly satisfied.
(d)   at the market price the amount sellers wish to sell is the same as the quantity buyers wish to buy.
(e)   the price is equal to the marginal utility of the good.

17 If it is said that there is excess demand for a commodity in a market in which demand curves slope down and supply curves slope up, this implies that

(a)   consumers are demanding more than they need.
(b)   the quantity supplied is in excess of that demanded.
(c)   price will tend to fall.
(d)   producers will tend to supply less of it.
(e)   market price is normally below equilibrium.

18 Consider two commodities A and B. When the price of A rises, <u>ceteris paribus</u>, the quantity of B demanded rises. Which of the following is correct?

(a)   A and B are in joint supply.
(b)   A and B are substitutes for each other.
(c)   A and B are complements to each other.
(d)   A is perfectly elastic in demand.
(e)   B is an inferior good.

19 The substitution effect of a fall in price

(a)   must more than offset the income effect.
(b)   cannot result in less being demanded.
(c)   must result in more being demanded.
(d)   cannot offset the income effect.
(e)   must have the same sign as the income effect.

20 If a good is an inferior good, then when its price falls

(a) the income and substitution effects must work in opposite directions.
(b) the substitution effect will lead to a fall and the income effect to a rise in the quantity demanded.
(c) both the income and the substitution effect will lead to a fall in the quantity demanded.
(d) the substitution effect will lead to a rise in the quantity demanded but the income effect may go in either direction.
(e) the income effect will lead to a fall in the quantity demanded but the substitution effect may go in either direction.

21 A consumer faces market prices of 30p for soap and 60p for shampoo. He allocates his expenditure so as to maximize his satisfaction and in so doing

(a) the marginal utility obtained from the last penny spent on shampoo is double that of the last penny spent on soap.
(b) the marginal utility of soap equals the marginal utility of shampoo.
(c) his total expenditure on soap equals his total expenditure on shampoo.
(d) his total utility from soap equals his total utility from shampoo.
(e) the marginal utility of soap is half that of shampoo.

22 The price of petrol is in equilibrium. A new device is invented which can reconvert the exhaust gases of car engines into petrol. Under which of the following assumptions is it most likely that the price of petrol would fall?

(a) Petrol has many alternative uses, the device is 100% efficient and its cost is high.
(b) Petrol has many alternative uses, the device is 50% efficient and its cost is high.
(c) Petrol has few alternative uses, the device is 50% efficient and its cost is high.
(d) Petrol has few alternative uses, the device is 100% efficient and its cost is low.
(e) Petrol has many alternative uses, the device is 100% efficient and its cost is low.

23 A necessary feature of a market in which the 'cobweb theorem' operates is that

(a) price moves gradually further and further away from equilibrium.
(b) quantity moves gradually further and further away from equilibrium.
(c) there is no equilibrium price and quantity.
(d) the elasticity of either demand or of supply (or both) must be equal to zero.
(e) the quantity supplied is not related to current market price.

24 The difference between the total utility in money terms derived by a consumer from a product and the total outlay on it could be considered a measure of the

(a) marginal utility of the product.
(b) price of the product.
(c) consumers' surplus from the product.
(d) elasticity of demand for the product.
(e) elasticity of supply of the product.

25

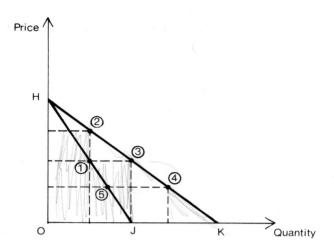

Fig. 2.3

In Fig. 2.3 HJ and HK are two demand curves and the numbers 1 to 5 are points on them. Which of the following statements is correct?

(a) Price elasticity at 1 is the same as at 2.
(b) Price elasticity at 1 is the same as at 3.
(c) Price elasticity at 4 is greater than at 3.
(d) Price elasticity at 2 is the same as at 4.
(e) Price elasticity at 4 is less than at 5.

26   Part of a demand schedule for peaches is shown below:

Price (pence)	Quantities demanded
5	100
6	60
7	35

Which of the following statements about the elasticity of demand is correct? (Note: For this question assume that percentage changes in price and quantity are calculated as percentages of the <u>original</u> price or quantity).

(a) Price rises from 5p to 6p, elasticity of demand = $(-)\frac{1}{2}$.
(b) Price rises from 5p to 6p, elasticity of demand = $(-)4$.
(c) Price falls from 6p to 5p, elasticity of demand = $(-)2$.
(d) Price falls from 7p to 6p, elasticity of demand = $(-)\frac{1}{5}$.
(e) Price rises from 6p to 7p, elasticity of demand = $(-)2\frac{1}{2}$.

27   Part of a demand schedule for pears is shown below:

Price (pence)	Quantities demanded
20	120
30	80
50	40

Use the formula for arc elasticity of demand to decide which of the following values are correct for price changes (i) between 20p and 30p and (ii) between 30p and 50p.

(a) $(-)\frac{2}{3}$
(b) $(-)\frac{3}{4}$
(c) $(-)1$
(d) $(-)1\frac{1}{3}$
(e) $(-)1.6$

28 The elasticity of demand for good A is greater than that for good B. Which of the following could explain this?

(a) B has more close substitutes than A.
(b) A is a normal good and B is not.
(c) A is an inferior good and consumers spend a higher proportion of their income on A than on B.
(d) A has more complements than B.
(e) A is a necessity and B is a luxury.

29 The elasticity of a straight-line demand curve

(a) must be equal to 0.
(b) must be equal to infinity.
(c) must be equal to 1.
(d) must be either 0 or infinity.
(e) may have varying values along its length.

30 If a price fall of 6% induces a fall in the quantity supplied of 3% the elasticity of supply is equal to

(a) 18.
(b) 6.
(c) 3.
(d) 2.
(e) ½.

31 An upward-sloping supply curve with elasticity equal to 1 appears on a graph as

(a) a rectangular hyperbola.
(b) a straight line parallel to the price axis.
(c) a straight line parallel to the quantity axis.
(d) a straight line through the origin.
(e) any straight line.

32 If the total expenditure (or outlay) by consumers on a particular product is always the same whatever price is charged for it, then

(a) demand must have an elasticity of unity.
(b) supply must have an elasticity of unity.
(c) increases or decreases in demand must always be exactly counterbalanced by increases or decreases in supply.
(d) the government must be imposing an equalizing tax.
(e) either the demand or the supply must have an elasticity equal to zero.

33 In a market where the product is in perfectly inelastic supply, the functions of prices are

1. to act as signals to producers to change output in accordance with consumer demand.
2. to act as signals to producers to use the most efficient combinations of factors of production.
3. to allocate output so that consumer satisfaction is maximized.
4. to allocate output so that consumers with the greatest needs consume most.

(a) 1,2,3 and 4 only
(b) 2 an 3 only
(c) 1 and 4 only
(d) 3 only
(e) None of the above because supply is fixed.

34 The government places a tax per unit on the producer of a good and the market price remains the same. Choose from the following list of elasticity conditions those which could account for this.

1. elasticity of supply = zero
2. elasticity of supply = infinity
3. elasticity of demand = zero
4. elasticity of demand = infinity

(a) 4 only
(b) 1 and 3 only
(c) 1 and 4 only
(d) 2 and 3 only
(e) 2 and 4 only

35 Suppose that the price of wheat fluctuates from year to year. The government decides to enter the market, buying and selling to prevent price falling below a certain level. At this level of price

(a) demand is now perfectly elastic.
(b) supply is now perfectly elastic.
(c) demand is now perfectly inelastic.
(d) supply is now perfectly inelastic.
(e) demand is now perfectly elastic and supply is perfectly elastic at the equilibrium price.

36 The following five markets are in equilibrium with a price of 50p and a quantity of 500. On which would the government choose to impose a unit tax of 50p if its only aim was to raise the maximum revenue for itself?

(a) Where the elasticity of supply is equal to infinity.
(b) Where the elasticity of supply is equal to unity.
(c) Where the elasticity of supply is equal to zero.
(d) Where the elasticity of demand is equal to infinity.
(e) Where the elasticity of demand is equal to unity.

37 If the equilibrium market price of a commodity is said to be stable, this means that

(a) the commodity is not an inferior good.
(b) deviations from equilibrium are self-restoring.
(c) either supply <u>or</u> demand is perfectly inelastic.
(d) the supply curve slopes downwards <u>or</u> the demand curve slopes upwards.
(e) <u>either</u> consumers are not trying to maximize their satisfaction <u>or</u> producers are not attempting to maximize their profits.

38

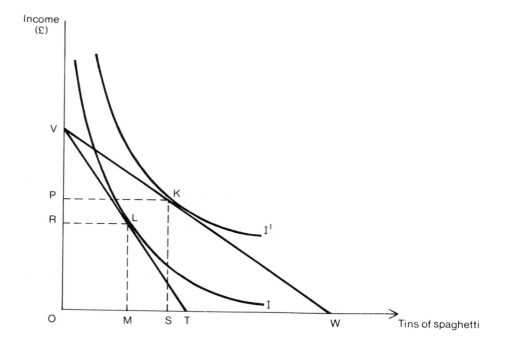

Fig. 2.4

In Fig. 2.4 a consumer is assumed to receive an income of OV and to have been faced with a budget line <u>last</u> week of VT. <u>This</u> week his budget line is VW. Two of his indifference curves are also shown. Which of the following statements is correct?

(a) The market price of spaghetti has fallen from OP to OR since last week.
(b) If the consumer had spent all his income on spaghetti he could have bought OM last week and OS this week.
(c) The consumer's real income has risen since last week from OR to OP.
(d) The consumer was in equilibrium last week at L, exchanging OR of his income for OM spaghetti.
(e) The consumer is in equilibrium this week at K, exchanging VP of his income for OS spaghetti.

39 An indifference curve for an individual consumer represents graphically

(a) the quantities of one good which are equal to quantities of another good.
(b) the way in which a consumer spends his income on two goods.
(c) the possible combinations of two goods which he can buy with his income.
(d) combinations of two goods which give him the same total satisfaction.
(e) combinations of two goods which have the same marginal utility.

40 An indifference curve is normally assumed to be convex to the origin because

(a) a consumer is assumed to maximize his satisfaction.
(b) the less one has of a good the lower its marginal utility.
(c) the price of a good tends to fall as consumption of it rises.
(d) the more one has of a good the less one needs of another good to compensate for the loss of a unit of it and retain the same total utility.
(e) a consumer needs more of one good to compensate for the loss of a unit of another and retain the same total utility.

41 If a consumer is allocating his income between two commodities in such a way that his budget line is at a tangent to an indifference curve he

(a) is buying too much of both goods.
(b) is buying the same quantity of each good.
(c) cannot increase his satisfaction without an increase in income.
(d) cannot be on the highest possible indifference curve.
(e) must be getting the same amount of satisfaction from each good.

42

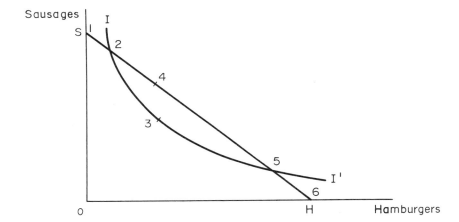

Fig. 2.5

Fig. 2.5 shows a consumer who is faced with a budget line SH. One of his indifference curves is also shown (I').   Points 1,2,3,4,5 and 6 represent different combinations of sausages and hamburgers which he consumes. Which of the following statements is correct?

(a) The consumer is indifferent between 1 and 6.
(b) The consumer is better off at 4 than at 2.
(c) The consumer is worse off at 5 than at 2.
(d) The consumer is indifferent between 2,4 and 5.
(e) The consumer has more hamburgers and more sausages at 4 than at 3.

Problems

1

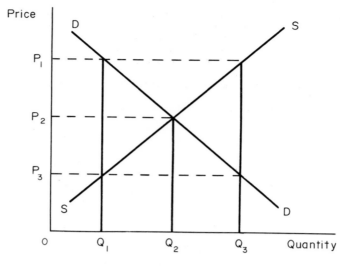

Fig. 2.6

Fig. 2.6 shows the supply and demand curves for a good.

   (i)   What is the equilibrium price?
  (ii)   What is the equilibrium quantity?
 (iii)   Supply falls to OQ_1. What price clears the market?
  (iv)   Supply rises to OQ_3. What price clears the market?
   (v)   The government imposes a legal maximum price of (a) OP_1, (b) OP_3. What is excess demand at each price?
  (vi)   The government imposes a legal minimum price of (a) OP_1, (b) OP_3. What is excess demand at each price?

2   The demand and supply schedules for an imaginary commodity are shown below:

Price (pence)	Weekly quantities	
	Demanded	Supplied
12	0	440
11	0	400
10	60	360
9	120	320
8	180	280
7	240	240
6	300	200
5	360	160
4	420	120
3	480	80
2	540	40
1	600	0

   (i)   Plot the two curves on graph paper.
  (ii)   What is the equilibrium price and quantity?

The following questions are independent. Changes mentioned are each from the original table.

 (iii)   There is a $33\frac{1}{3}\%$ fall in demand. What is the new equilibrium price and quantity?
  (iv)   Demand is as in the original table, but the quantity supplied rises by 50%. What is the new equilibrium price and quantity?
   (v)   Demand increases by 200 units regardless of price and supply falls by 100 units at every price. What is the new equilibrium price and quantity?
  (vi)   Demand falls by a third, but supply is perfectly inelastic at the original equilibrium quantity. What is the equilibrium market price?
 (vii)   Supply increases by 50%, but market price remains fixed by the government at the original equilibrium level. What is the level of excess demand or supply?

3 In Fig. 2.7, DD and SS represent the annual demand and supply for record-players. Indicate the numbers and/or letters of the curves shown which represent the appropriate demand and supply situation in the following circumstances:

   (i)   The price of records rises.
   (ii)   The price of valves and transistors rises.
   (iii) The quality of records increases.
   (iv)   Productivity in the record-player industry rises.
   (v)   There is a change in tastes from recorded to live music.
   (vi)   There is a rise in the price of tape-recorders.
   (vii) A general rise in wages occurs.
   (viii) The wages of workers in the radio components industry rises.
   (ix)   Consumers' incomes rise.
   (x)   Producers spend more on advertising per unit of output.

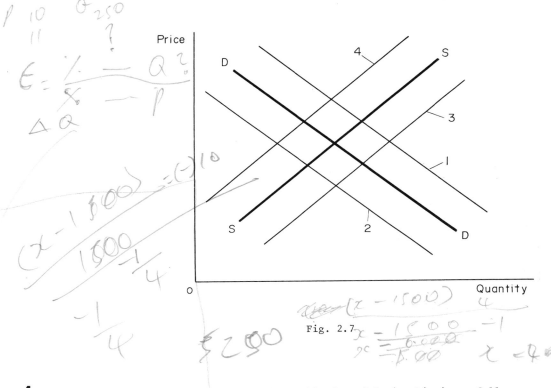

Fig. 2.7

4 A seller of lemonade estimates that the weekly demand facing him is as follows:

Price (pence)	10	9	8	7	6	5	4
Quantity	250	350	500	600	700	1000	1500

   (i)   The market price is 10p. What is the elasticity of demand for a reduction to 9p?
   (ii)   The market price is 5p. What is the elasticity of demand for an increase to 6p?
   (iii) The market price changes between 6p and 7p. What is the elasticity of demand between these prices? (Use the formula for the arc elasticity of demand or examine total revenue at the two prices.)
   (iv)   Price is raised from 10p to 11p and the elasticity of demand is found to be (-)6. How many would be demanded at the higher price?
   (v)   Price is lowered from 4p to 3p and the elasticity of demand is found to be (-)10. How many would be demanded at the lower price?

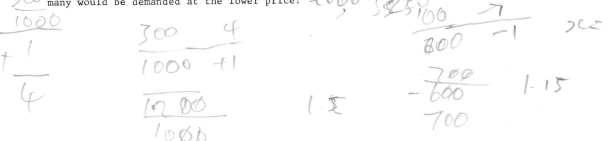

5 Points A to H in Fig. 2.8 represent different price and quantity combinations on two demand curves.

    (i)   Which has/have elasticity equal to 0?
    (ii)   Which has/have elasticity equal to (−)1?
    (iii) Which has/have elasticity equal to (−) infinity?
    (iv)   Which has the greater elasticity, A or C?
    (v)   Which has the greater elasticity, A or D?
    (vi)   Which has the greater elasticity, A or B?
    (vii) Estimate (graphically) the elasticity of demand at B.
    (viii) Estimate (graphically) the elasticity of demand at C.
    (ix)   Estimate (graphically) the elasticity of demand at D.

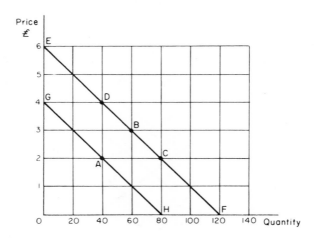

Fig. 2.8

6 Curves A to F on Fig. 2.9 represent six supply curves. At price OP:

    (i)   Which has/have elasticity equal to 0?
    (ii)   Which has/have elasticity equal to 1?
    (iii) Which has/have elasticity equal to infinity?
    (iv)   Which has/have elasticity greater than 1?
    (v)   Which has/have elasticity less than 1?
    (vi)   Which has/have negative elasticity?

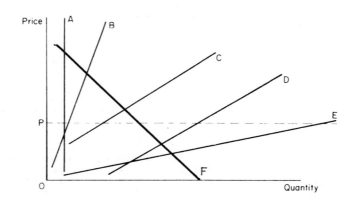

Fig. 2.9

7 The following questions relate to the five supply and demand diagrams in Fig. 2.10, which are drawn to the same scale. In which of them:

   (i)   is the good with the best substitutes?
  (ii)   is the good which can least easily be increased or decreased in supply?
 (iii)   is the supply or demand perfectly elastic?
  (iv)   is the elasticity of supply or demand equal to unity at equilibrium?
   (v)   is there a good subject to falling production costs?
  (vi)   would the imposition of a minimum price of OP be most likely to lead to unsold stocks?
 (vii)   would the imposition of a given unit tax raise most revenue for the government?
(viii)   would the imposition of a given unit tax have least effect upon market price?
  (ix)   is there an inferior good?
   (x)   is the consumers' surplus zero at equilibrium?
  (xi)   is there a Giffen good?
 (xii)   is equilibrium unstable? (Assume that there are no time lags.)

For the following questions ignore diagram V, and choose only from I to IV:

(xiii)   In which is the elasticity of demand greater than that of supply at equilibrium? (Ignore signs.)
 (xiv)   In which would the imposition of a maximum price of OP be most likely to lead to queues or black markets?

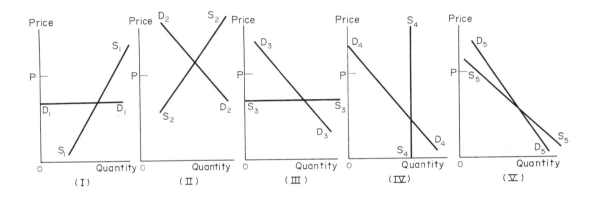

Fig. 2.10

8 In a market for pots of ginger, there are two consumers, Alan and Bob, whose demands are as in the following table:

Price (pence)	Annual demand by	
	Alan	Bob
50	0	5
40	10	10
30	15	20
20	20	30
10	25	40

   (i)   Plot Alan's and Bob's demand curves on graph paper.
  (ii)   Plot the market demand curve.
 (iii)   If Alan buys 15 pots of ginger, how much will he be prepared to pay for them?
  (iv)   If the price falls from 40p to 30p, by how much will Alan increase his consumption?
   (v)   If Bob buys 20 pots, what is the marginal utility of ginger to him?
  (vi)   If Bob buys 10 pots, what is their total utility to him? (Assume that the marginal utility of the first five pots is the same and that of the second five pots is also the same.)
 (vii)   Which demand curve has the highest elasticity for a price fall from 30p to 20p, Alan's or Bob's?
(viii)   Which demand curve has the highest elasticity for a price fall from 30p to 20p, Alan's, Bob's or the market demand?
  (ix)   If the assumptions of (vi) hold and market price is 40p, what is Bob's consumer surplus?

9 Careful questioning of a housewife reveals that she gets the same total satisfaction from each of the following combinations of oranges and bananas per week:

16 oranges and 1 banana
12 oranges and 3 bananas
 9 oranges and 5 bananas
 4 oranges and 14 bananas
 1 orange and 30 bananas

(i) On graph paper plot the points on her indifference curve implied by the above. Join them in a smooth curve.

(ii) Estimate from the graph the approximate number of bananas which would be needed with 6 oranges to give the same satisfaction as the other combinations.

(iii) How many bananas would be needed to compensate for a decrease in orange consumption from 9 to 4?

(iv) Oranges cost 10p each and bananas cost 8p each, and her housekeeping allowance is just sufficient to allow her to buy 20 oranges. What is the maximum number of bananas she could buy if she did not buy any oranges?

(v) Bananas cost 4p each and the housekeeping allowance is just sufficient for her to buy 30. If she spent all the available allowance on oranges, however, she could buy only 10. What is the price of an orange?

(vi) Oranges are the same price as bananas, and the available housekeeping allowance is £1.40, with which she can buy either 14 oranges and no bananas or 14 bananas and no oranges. What is the price of a banana?

(vii) Draw the budget line indicated by the information in (vi) above on the graph used for the answer to (i) above. Estimate approximately the number of oranges and bananas she should buy to maximize her satisfaction.

(viii) The price of bananas falls by 50% from (vii) above, while the price of oranges and the housekeeping allowance remain the same. How many bananas can she buy now with her entire allowance?

(ix) Draw the budget line indicated by the information in (viii) above on the same graph used for (i) and (vii). Estimate approximately the number of oranges and bananas which will now maximize the housewife's satisfaction if you are told that she is also indifferent between the following combinations:

20 oranges and 4 bananas
16 oranges and 5 bananas
12 oranges and 8 bananas
 7 oranges and 14 bananas
 5 oranges and 22 bananas

(x) Estimate from the graph approximately how much of the changed consumption of bananas is due to the income effect and how much to the substitution effect of the price change.

10 In Fig. 2.11 a consumer is assumed to receive an income of OA which he spends on all goods he wishes to buy except nuts. Two of his indifference curves are also shown. He is assumed to maximize his satisfaction.

Questions (i) to (iv) assume that the price of nuts relative to all other goods is measured by the slope of AB.

(i) How many nuts can he buy if he spends all his income on nuts?

(ii) How many nuts does he buy?

(iii) How much of his income does he spend on nuts?

(iv) What is his marginal rate of substitution between nuts and all other goods in equilibrium?

The price of nuts now falls to $\frac{OA}{OC}$, income remaining constant.

(v) How many more nuts does he buy?

(vi) How much of his income does he keep for all other goods?

(vii) How much extra satisfaction does he obtain?

(viii) How much of the changed demand for nuts is due to the income effect and how much to the substitution effect of the change in price?

(ix) Which lettered points are on the consumer's income consumption curve and which are on the price consumption curve?

(x) Assume again that the price of nuts is given by the slope of AB and that the consumer buys the quantity given in the answer to (ii) above. Now assume there is a ban on nut consumption. How much additional income would he need to compensate exactly for not being allowed to buy any nuts at the market price?

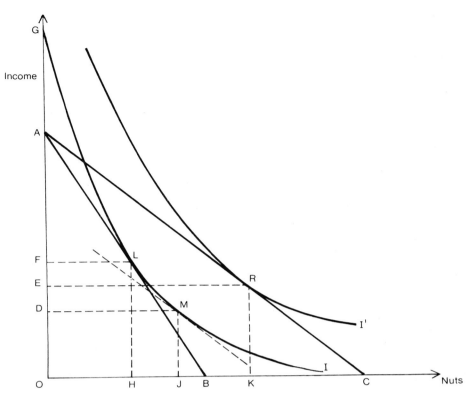

Fig. 2.11

U.K. ECONOMY

Exercises

Note: Sources are suggested for all exercises. Alternatives may be available if the one mentioned is not in your library. For advice on them and on the collection and presentation of data in tabular and graphical form see pp. ix-x.

1 Find out the average 'farm gate' price of potatoes and total potato production for two recent and consecutive years. (Source: <u>Annual Abstract of Statistics</u>.)

(i) Assuming <u>ceteris paribus</u>, calculate a measure of the elasticity of demand for potatoes taking the price and quantity in the earlier year as the bases for the calculation.

(ii) Still assuming <u>ceteris paribus</u>, calculate the arc elasticity of demand for potatoes. Is this an improvement on (i) above?

(iii) Give as many reasons as you can why it may be unrealistic to make the <u>ceteris paribus</u> assumptions mentioned above. Why, however, is it necessary to do so in order to estimate price elasticity?

2 Complete the following table with data from two consecutive years:

	Personal income (i)	% Change in (i) (ii)	Consumers' expenditure at constant prices			
			Food expenditure (iii)	% Change in (iii) (iv)	Travel expenditure (v)	% Change in (v) (vi)
Year 19....						
Year 19....						

Source: Annual Abstract of Statistics

(i) Calculate estimates of the income elasticity of demand for food and for travel. Which is higher and what does that imply?

(ii) What assumptions were you making implicitly in calculating elasticities in this way? How reasonable do you think they are?

3 The Nationwide Building Society publishes a Bulletin showing quarterly changes in the average price of houses. Obtain a copy and note the average price of all properties for each of the last five years. Extract also the total numbers of permanent dwellings completed in the same years. Prepare a graph and plot the two series.

  (i)   Is there any observable relationship between price and production over the period?
 (ii)   Examine the graph to see if there might be a better association between the price of houses and the number of dwellings completed the <u>following</u> year. Can you think of any reasons why this might be the case?
(iii)   In so far as you may have observed a statistical association between the price of houses and house construction, do you think this is more likely to be due to the nature of the demand curve, of the supply curve, both or neither?

4 Plot on graph paper the price index and the production index for clothing and footwear for each of the last 5 or 10 years. (Source: <u>Annual Abstract of Statistics.</u>) Label each point with a date and join them with a dotted line.

  (i)   What, if anything, does the line represent?
 (ii)   On the same graph now plot an index of consumers' expenditure on clothing and footwear for the same years. What different interpretation would you place on the new curve and that plotted first?

5 Obtain a copy of either <u>Parker's Car Price Guide</u> or the <u>Motorist's Guide to New and Used Car Prices</u>. Note the current second-hand and the new original price of the following two-year-old cars:

        small Ford car
        medium-size British Leyland saloon
        Japanese car
        Rolls Royce or Mercedes Benz car

  (i)   Which car has depreciated most and least relative to the new price?
 (ii)   How far do you think that the answer to (i) above can be explained in terms of supply and demand?

6 Find out from your nearest travel agent the cost of the following journeys:

        London to New York by air, tourist class scheduled fare
        London to New York by the cheapest route
        Glasgow to Manchester by train, second class
        Piccadilly Circus to Marble Arch by underground

Calculate the cost per mile in each case. How can you explain the differences?

7 Ask ten members of your class or group how many bars of fruit and nut milk chocolate he or she would buy per week at each of a range of prices. Select the range as follows: take the current market price as the middle value; choose higher and lower prices at intervals of roughly 10% of market price to the nearest penny. Fill in as many columns as you can in the table.

Price	Quantities demanded by individuals										Total demand
	1	2	3	4	5	6	7	8	9	10	

From the date in the table construct demand curves for each individual and for the whole class.

  (i)   Do they all exhibit downward slopes?
 (ii)   Are they all 'rational'?
(iii)   At current market price, how many bars would be bought?
 (iv)   Suppose that the class buys that number of bars which results in marginal utility being equal to market price. Assume that the price which the class would have been prepared to pay for each of these units can be considered as a monetary measure of the utility derived from its consumption. Calculate the total utility derived by the class from the consumption of the total number of units bought. To obtain a measure of consumer surplus subtract the total cost to the class of all units from the total utility you have calculated. Give a verbal interpretation of the amount of consumer surplus.

Essays

1. Consider the likely economic effects on supply, demand and price of one of the following:

   (a) a substantial fall in productivity in the production of soap
   (b) the discovery of a cancer risk in potatoes
   (c) a general drop in average winter temperatures in Britain
   (d) a plague of woodworm in the country
   (e) the discovery that tobacco can be made from grass
   (f) a return to popularity of the hat as part of masculine dress

2. Examine the validity of the following statement: 'It is only in market equilibrium that the quantity sold is equal to the quantity bought, that excess demand is zero and that any change in price acts to restore equilibrium.'

3. If it rained lager, would water be as expensive as beer?

4. 'The main function of the price mechanism is to ration scarce goods among a number of consumers.' Discuss.

5. 'Rational consumers prefer necessities to luxuries, so the prices of the former tend to be higher than those of the latter.' Do you agree? Could the hypothesis be put to the test?

6. How far is it true to say that the consumer ultimately decides what goods shall be produced in a market economy?

7. What do you consider would be the likely consequences of a new law making it an offence for price differences between products not to reflect cost differences? Would it make any difference if the law referred to quality differences rather than to costs?

8. How far is it true to say that the factors determining the demand for a good are all different from the factors determining supply?

9. Consider the effects of allowing taxis to carry two charging meters, a high rate meter for times when it is raining and a low rate meter for other times.

10. Discuss the proposition that legally imposed maximum prices benefit all consumers while minimum prices benefit all producers.

11. Fares on the London Tube vary with distance; those on the Paris Metro are standardized per journey regardless distance. Compare the economic effects of the two systems.

12. How far can it be said that demand curves slope downwards for the opposite reason that supply curves slope upwards?

13. 'If the demand for agricultural products was more elastic, governments would not need to bother with stabilization policies for the industry.' Discuss.

14. Explain, with particular reference to the elasticity of demand and supply, what type of goods would be chosen for taxation by a government which wished to raise the most revenue for itself consistent with the minimum price rise to consumers.

15. Compare the effects of a unit tax on mirrors with one on cheddar cheese.

16. Explain carefully the difference between the income effect and the substitution effect of a price change. What implications do they have for the shape of demand curves?

17. Are middlemen who sell Wimbledon tickets at inflated prices sharks, benefactors or neither?

18. Two firms in a city centre allocate their limited parking spaces to employees. Firm A holds a monthly auction and Firm B used a system based on need and length of service. Compare the economic effects of the two systems.

19. Is there any truth in the hypothesis that the elasticity of demand for necessities tends to be less than that for luxuries?

20. What sort of product do you imagine would be likely to have a normal price elasticity and a negative income elasticity of demand?

21. To what extent is it true that black markets follow when the price mechanism is not allowed to work?

22. Why might governments be less inclined to intervene in agricultural markets if demand elasticity was equal to unity? Would there remain any reasons for intervention?

23. 'When a tax is put on nuts, the price rises to the consumer. This rise in price reduces demand and increases supply. There is therefore no reason why the price may not return to the original equilibrium.' Discuss.

24. What can be said about the elasticity of demand for a product if total revenue rises when price is lowered and also when it is raised?

25. 'Advertisers buy time on commercial television if programmes are popular. The BBC receives the revenue from the sale of licences at a fixed price to viewers. Therefore commercial television better satisfies the wishes of the consuming public.' Discuss this argument.

26. Discuss the case for allowing tenants of Council houses to sub-let them at the free market price.

27. 'There is no reason why indifference curves cannot intersect each other since a consumer may quite reasonably change his preferences as time passes.' Discuss.

28. What is the relationship between a consumer's indifference map and his/her conventional demand curve for a product?

CHAPTER 3

Production: Costs and Organization

This chapter is devoted to factors lying behind the supply curve for a product. It focuses on costs of production and the way in which they influence the decisions of business firms in different market situations.

The supply curve of an industry is made up of the supply curves of the individual firms within it. Each firm is normally assumed to be trying to maximize its profits and the THEORY OF THE FIRM is concerned with analysing how a business decides upon its most profitable output. The maximum profit position is described as the equilibrium of the firm.

Emphasis here is concentrated upon the costs of producing different quantities of a commodity (sometimes known as the COST FUNCTION). Implicit in costs are the alternative ways in which a given output can be produced utilizing different combinations of factors of production (known as the PRODUCTION FUNCTION). The nature of costs normally varies according to the length of time allowed. In the SHORT RUN some factors of production (or INPUTS) are FIXED, and their costs likewise. These fixed, or OVERHEAD COSTS, such as that of a durable machine used in a factory, are sometimes called SUPPLEMENTARY or INDIRECT costs to distinguish them from the VARIABLE, DIRECT or PRIME COSTS, which vary directly as output changes. The LONG RUN is defined as the period within which all costs can be varied. Sometimes a further period, the VERY LONG RUN, is distinguished, when new products and processes can be considered by a firm.

In the short run, the existence of fixed costs means that the AVERAGE (or UNIT) TOTAL COSTS (A.T.C) of production start to fall, as fixed costs are spread over larger outputs, until a point is reached where the fixed supply of a factor begins to push A.T.C. up. This gives rise to what is known as the 'U-SHAPED' COST CURVE. AVERAGE FIXED COSTS (A.F.C.) fall as output expands. AVERAGE VARIABLE COSTS (A.V.C.) tend to be U-shaped in the short-run (owing to the Principle of Diminishing Returns; see next chapter). It should be added that falling costs may be INTERNAL to the firm, or EXTERNAL, where they are due to expansion of the whole industry. When output is such that A.T.C. are at a minimum the firm is sometimes said to be of OPTIMUM SIZE, though it should be noted that this is not necessarily its most profitable output.

A firm maximizes profits, or minimizes losses, by producing that output where the addition to total cost which it incurs by producing one more unit is neither more nor less than the addition to the total revenue which it receives from sales. That is to say, MARGINAL COST (M.C.) is equal to MARGINAL REVENUE (M.R.). If also AVERAGE REVENUE (A.R.) is not less than A.T.C. this will be its long-run equilibrium position and ensure that the firm continues in business, since A.T.C. is defined to include the NORMAL PROFITS (or the opportunity cost of capital) necessary to keep the firm in the industry. In the short run, however, the firm will not shut down unless A.R. is also less than A.V.C.

The behaviour of a firm depends not only on its costs but also on the market situation in which it operates. Two limiting cases are usually referred to initially — PERFECT COMPETITION and MONOPOLY.

Perfect competition has the distinguishing feature that firms are PRICE TAKERS, i.e. each is faced with a price over which it has no influence whatsoever. Such a situation would follow from more than one set of assumptions. The most common is the existence of a very large number of independent firms selling an identical product in a market where every buyer is aware of the price asked by every seller. The demand curve facing such a firm (though not the industry) is horizontal, or perfectly elastic. Marginal revenue is the same as price, or average revenue, and the maximum profit (equilibrium) output is where M.C. is equal to price as well as to M.C. In the long run, perfect competition assumes the freedom of firms to enter the industry. Abnormally large profits — total revenue greater than total costs — encourage new firms to come in; losses cause firms to leave. In the equilibrium of the industry firms produce where price = A.R. = A.C. = M.R. = M.C. and no firms are entering or leaving the industry. They receive exactly enough revenue to cover all costs including normal profits.

A monopoly exists when a firm is the sole seller in an industry. A monopolist is not a price taker, but is faced with a less than perfectly elastic demand curve. Increases in its sales can be achieved only at the cost of lowering price to the consumer. For this reason the marginal revenue curve of a monopolist lies below the demand curve (or average revenue curve). Equilibrium output is where M.C. = M.R., but price is above this. Whether the monopolist is making abnormally large profits, however, depends upon whether A.R. is greater than A.T.C. In any event, in the monopoly case there are BARRIERS TO ENTRY for new firms into the industry. Such barriers may be due to low costs, product differentiation, legal, regional, institutional or other factors. It should be noted, too, that there is no supply curve for a monopolist, for whom the amount offered for sale at any price depends on the nature and elasticity of demand for the product and not solely on costs of production.

Pure monopoly, as also perfect competition, is an abstraction of economists, but firms do tend to be, or not to be, price takers. A firm possesses a degree of monopoly power where there are few substitutes for its product and it is, to a degree, insulated from the actions of other sellers. This is likely when costs of production fall continuously over a large range of output, so that a single large firm is capable of being more efficient than a number of small ones. Such falling costs or ECONOMIES OF LARGE-SCALE PRODUCTION are sometimes traced to technical, managerial or commercial (e.g. marketing, financial or risk-bearing) causes. When the optimum size of a firm is such as to enable it to produce the entire industry output, it is known as a NATURAL MONOPOLY.

Firms may grow and achieve monopoly power through MERGERS, amalgamating with other firms. It is common in such cases to describe amalgamations as involving either HORIZONTAL or VERTICAL INTEGRATION. The former concerns firms in the same kind of business. The latter involves businesses at different stages of the production process and may be forwards towards the final consumer or backwards to earlier stages of production. A third type of merger, known as CONGLOMERATE, occurs when the firms affected operate in separate markets. Monopoly power is also obtainable by agreements between firms to control, e.g. price or output, through cartels, trade associations etc. In such cases, effective monopoly power rests on the extent to which control of entry can be maintained.

IMPERFECT COMPETITION, which does not extend to the extremes of perfect competition or monopoly, tends to typify most industries in the real world. Imperfections arise from the existence of PRODUCT DIFFERENTIATION, real and imaginary, sometimes resulting from advertising and other sales expenditures. It also follows from the fact that the number of sellers of a product is small enough for firms to have to take account of the reactions of rivals to their own price or output policies. The former situation is often referred to as MONOPOLISTIC COMPETITION and the latter is called OLIGOPOLY.

The market behaviour of a firm is, in practice, influenced by the institutional organization within which it carries on business. The following forms are usually distinguished: private enterprise, consisting of ONE-MAN BUSINESSES (or SINGLE PROPRIETORSHIPS), which have a single owner; PARTNERSHIPS which are normally owned by two to twenty persons; JOINT-STOCK COMPANIES (or corporations) which may have many more owners, and CO-OPERATIVES which are 'owned' by the customers of the business. Public enterprise consists of PUBLIC CORPORATIONS which are NATIONALIZED INDUSTRIES owned by the government, though they are largely operated as independent concerns, and municipal undertakings.

The main form of private business organization in Britain is the joint-stock company. Its advantage arises from the legal principle of LIMITED LIABILITY, which assists in the raising of large amounts of capital. In return, companies must disclose some information about their activities. In the case of large PUBLIC COMPANIES this means publishing Profit and Loss Accounts and Balance Sheets. Companies secure new funds by the issue of (stocks and) SHARES, the principal types of which are ORDINARY shares (or equities) and PREFERENCE shares. They also raise capital through the issue of FIXED INTEREST stock (DEBENTURES or LOAN STOCK). Equity holders are the true owners of the business. Their income, received as DIVIDENDS on shares, usually reflects the profitability of the firm. The control which they exercise over the business depends substantially on the voting and other rights attaching to their shares, which include the power to appoint directors to run a business for them. In some modern large corporations with thousands of small shareholders, effective control of a business may, however, lie with the directors. It may also, to a considerable extent, be in the hands of financial institutions, such as banks and insurance companies, which have assumed a major role in Britain in recent years. Divorce of ownership from control, it should be noted, may imply that firms do not try to maximize their profits. Alternative goals include the maximization of the sales or growth of the firm, perhaps with a minimum profit sub-goal, or even maintaining a 'quiet life' for the decision takers. Such goals are usually bound up with the existence of imperfect competition. They also call for different analyses of the behaviour of the firm from the traditional one.

ANALYSIS

Multiple Choice

Choose the alternative which provides the best answer to the question or completes the sentence most satisfactorily.

1 Choose from the following list of costs those which vary with output:

1. Prime
2. Supplementary
3. Indirect
4. Marginal
5. Overhead
6. Fixed
7. Direct

(a) 2,3,5 and 6 only
(b) 1,4 and 7 only
(c) 1,3 and 7 only
(d) 2 and 4 only
(e) 4 only

2 The long run from the point of view of the firm is

  (a) three months or over.
  (b) six months or over.
  (c) one year or over.
  (d) five years or over.
  (e) All of the above could be correct.

3

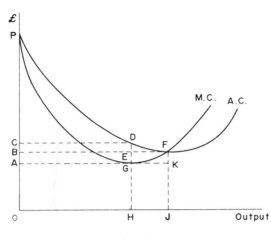

Fig. 3.1

Fig. 3.1 shows the average and marginal cost curves for a firm.

  (i) Which of the following represents the total costs of producing OH output?

      (a) OPGH
      (b) OPDH
      (c) OHGA
      (d) ACDG
      (e) None of the above

  (ii) Which of the following represents the <u>change</u> in total costs following an increase in output
       from OH to OJ?

      (a) OPGFJ
      (b) FJ
      (c) GH
      (d) HEFJ minus BCDE
      (e) None of the above

*If Norm prof not obtain cost will
op cost will mov to next best thing*

4 Normal profit is a term used by economists to refer to

  (a) the difference between total costs and total revenue.
  (b) the difference between marginal costs and marginal revenue.
  (c) the opportunity cost of capital.
  (d) profit earned in a normal or average year.
  (e) the net profit paid out as dividends to shareholders.

5 Which of the following list of costs is most likely to vary with the output of a motor manufacturer
during a period of a year?

  (a) The salary of the managing director
  (b) The rent of the factory
  (c) The wages of the workers in the paint shop
  (d) The interest paid on a loan used for general purposes   *fixed cost*
  (e) The cost of drilling machinery used

6 Economies of large-scale production exist because

  (a) large machines are more economical than small.
  (b) managements can look after quite large enterprises.
  (c) it is easier for a large firm to borrow money than for a small firm.
  (d) production must be on a large scale before full use can be made of some machinery.
  (e) All of the above can cause large-scale economies.

WIIE - D

7 By the U-shaped cost curve is meant the tendency for

(a) average fixed costs to fall at first and then rise.
(b) marginal costs to rise at first and then fall.
(c) total costs to fall at first and then rise.
(d) average total costs to fall at first and then rise.
(e) marginal revenue to fall at first and then rise.

8 When average cost is falling, marginal cost

(a) must be falling faster than average cost.
(b) must be less than average cost.
(c) may be either greater, less than or equal to average cost.
(d) cannot be falling.
(e) must be greater than average cost.

9 External economies are said to exist when the average costs of production fall as a result of

(a) the expansion of the output of an industry.
(b) additional advertising and sales expenditure by a firm.
(c) a firm reaching a size where it can purchase factors of production at lower prices.
(d) a firm increasing its inputs of factors of production.
(e) a firm being able to lower the cost of raising capital because of its size.

10 If the total cost curve of a firm is an upward-sloping straight line through the origin

(a) average costs are rising, but marginal costs may be rising or falling.
(b) marginal and average costs are rising.
(c) fixed costs are zero.
(d) total revenue is constant.
(e) the firm is operating in conditions of perfect competition.

11 A firm will shut down rather than carry on producing in the short run if

(a) average revenue is less than average total cost.
(b) total revenue is less than total variable cost.
(c) marginal revenue is less than marginal cost.
(d) price is less than average revenue.
(e) marginal revenue is less than average revenue.

12 Under perfect competition all but one of the following statements are correct. Which is the exception?

(a) Any firm will find that it is unable to sell any output at all if it charges a price above the market equilibrium price.
(b) All firms maximize profits at the point where there marginal costs are equal to marginal revenue.
(c) All firms face exactly the same perfectly elastic demand curve.
(d) The market demand curve consists of the sum of the demand curves of individual firms.
(e) The market supply curve consists of the sum of the marginal costs curves of individual firms.

13 If the total revenue curve facing a firm is a straight line through the origin

(a) the equilibrium output of the firm will be infinitely large.
(b) it is impossible to know from this information alone how competitive the market is for the firm.
(c) it is impossible to know whether marginal revenue is rising, falling or constant.
(d) price is equal to marginal revenue.
(e) there are no fixed costs.

14 The standard analysis of the behaviour of a profit-maximizing firm in the long run assumes which of the following (i) under perfect competition and (ii) under monopoly?

1. Marginal cost equals marginal revenue.
2. Marginal cost equals average cost.
3. Marginal cost equals average revenue.

(a) 1 only
(b) 1 and 2 only
(c) 2 and 3 only
(d) 1 and 3 only
(e) 1,2 and 3

15 A profit-maximizing monopolist will

   (a) set price so that the addition to total revenue is equal to marginal cost.
   (b) set price and output so that marginal revenue is at a maximum.
   (c) produce the quantity which sells at the highest price.
   (d) produce the quantity which costs least to produce.
   (e) set price to equal marginal cost.

16

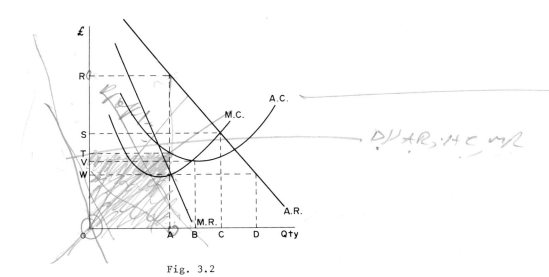

Fig. 3.2

Fig. 3.2 portrays the cost and revenue curves facing a profit-maximizing monopolist.

(i) What are equilibrium output and market price?

    (a) Output OA and price OR
    (b) Output OB and price OV
    (c) Output OC and price OS
    (d) Output OD and price OW
    (e) None of the above

(ii) What is supernormal monopoly profit?

    (a) RS times OA
    (b) RT times OA
    (c) OR times OA
    (d) SW times OA
    (e) OS times OC

17 Choose from the following list of assumptions those which are normally considered typical of an industry classified under the head of monopolistic competition.

   1. Free entry of firms   5. Economics of scale
   2. Barriers to entry   6. Large number of firms
   3. A homogeneous product   7. Few firms
   4. A differentiated product   8. Firms earn more than normal profit in the long run

   (a) 1,4 and 6 only
   (b) 2,7 and 8 only
   (c) 2,3,5 and 7 only
   (d) 2,5 and 6 only
   (e) 1,3,7 and 8 only

18 Consider two profit-maximizing firms, one in a perfectly competitive market, the other a monopolist. Compared to the former the monopolist will

   (a) tend to use less efficient combinations of inputs.
   (b) produce a larger output.
   (c) operate where marginal cost is not equal to but less than price.
   (d) operate where average costs are at a minimum.
   (e) operate where price is not equal to but less than marginal revenue.

19 Advertising expenditure may be used by a firm for all except one of the following purposes. Which is the exception?

   (a) Lowering the elasticity of demand for its product
   (b) Making its product seem less like that of its competitors
   (c) Attracting new firms into the industry
   (d) Allowing it to take advantage of economies of scale
   (e) Increasing its share of the market

20 Oligopoly is distinguished by the fact that

   (a) each firm in the industry produces a different product.
   (b) firms produce several different products.
   (c) there are relatively few firms in the industry.
   (d) firms are faced with relatively few consumers.
   (e) the industry is dominated by a single firm.

21 If a firm is making only normal profits, it

   (a) cannot be a monopolist.
   (b) will not leave the industry in the long run.
   (c) cannot be maximizing its profits.
   (d) must be operating under conditions of perfect competition.
   (e) will be operating at the point where marginal cost exactly equals marginal revenue.

22 If a firm raises its price and total revenue rises it knows that

   (a) it should immediately restore price to the original level.
   (b) it should cut price below the previous level.
   (c) the elasticity of demand for its product must be less than unity.
   (d) the elasticity of demand for its product may be greater than unity.
   (e) other firms also are not raising their prices.

23 If an industry is characterized by the presence of a large number of firms producing differentiated products, it is said to be

   (a) perfectly competitive.
   (b) monopolistically competitive.
   (c) oligopolistic.
   (d) monopolistic.
   (e) None of the above.

24 The reason why it is normally impossible to construct a supply curve for a monopolist is that

   (a) the monopolist does not really know what demand curve it is facing.
   (b) it is impossible to know whether other firms will come into the industry.
   (c) monopolists are known to be trying to maximize sales not profits.
   (d) there is no unique quantity supplied at a given price.
   (e) a monopolist usually operates under conditions of falling average costs.

25 Which of the following statements about imperfect competition is generally correct?

   (a) In oligopoly, the equilibrium of the firm cannot be determined without knowledge of the reactions rival firms make to the price policy of other firms.
   (b) A major difference between monopolistic and perfect competition is that it is only in the former that a profit-maximizing firm will equate marginal cost and marginal revenue.
   (c) In oligopoly, firms do not aim at profit maximization but at sales maximization so long as they do not make losses.
   (d) In monopolistic competition a firm knows that if it raises the price of its product its rivals will follow suit, but if it lowers price they will not.
   (e) In industries classed under the heads of both oligopoly and monopolistic competition, variations in price, in sales expenditures and product differentiation are liable to be found.

26 For which of the following ways of raising capital do the costs to the firm vary with its profits?

   (a) Ordinary shares
   (b) Debentures
   (c) Bank loans
   (d) Bank overdrafts
   (e) Convertible loan stock

27 Which of the following holders of a company's issued capital is likely to receive the biggest relative increase in income if there is a substantial increase in profits?

(a)   A 6½% cumulative preference shareholder
(b)   A 7% preference shareholder
(c)   A 7½% debenture holder
(d)   A holder of 8% unsecured loan stock
(e)   An ordinary shareholder

28 A holder of 40% of the voting equity in a company will be more likely to be in a position to control its activities

(a)   the more other equity holders there are.
(b)   the greater the degree of monopoly exercised by the firm.
(c)   the more chance there is of a take-over bid.
(d)   the longer the company has been in existence.
(e)   None of the above, because 50% is the minimum holding necessary to control a company.

29 Who controls the day-to-day action in a joint-stock company?

(a)   The shareholders
(b)   The debenture holders
(c)   The company chairman
(d)   The salaried managers
(e)   Consumers of the product

30 If an industry is said to have a 3-firm (output) concentration ratio of 40%, this means that

(a)   it is highly competitive.
(b)   40% of the firms produce 3% of the industry output.
(c)   the three largest firms produce 40% of the industry output.
(d)   the share of the top three firms in total output has grown by 40% over a stated period.
(e)   3% of the firms in the industry account for 40% of the industry output.

31 Mergers can be either vertical, horizontal or conglomerate. Which of the following is a horizontal merger?

(a)   A shoe manufacturer merges with a shoe retailer
(b)   A shoe manufacturer merges with a tannery
(c)   A shoe manufacturer merges with a sock manufacturer
(d)   A shoe manufacturer merges with another shoe manufacturer
(e)   None of the above

32 A public enterprise is distinguished from a private enterprise by whether it

(a)   is making a loss on its trading account.
(b)   is owned by the government.
(c)   is owned by more than seven persons.
(d)   has issued shares to the general public.
(e)   is a co-operative owned by the public who are its customers.

33 In a joint-stock company, the ordinary shareholders

(a)   have unlimited liability for the company's debts.
(b)   do not have the right to attend the annual general meeting of the company.
(c)   receive the company's profits each year in the form of dividends.
(d)   have a higher priority to dividends than preference shareholders.
(e)   do not have the right to appoint the chief sales manager.

34 Which of the following items would appear in a company's profit and loss account rather than in its balance sheet?

(a)   Value of stocks of raw materials held
(b)   Total issued capital
(c)   Amounts owed to the company's creditors
(d)   Revenue from sales of the company's products
(e)   Cash held at the bank

35 Which of the following totals would appear in a company's balance sheet rather than in its profit and loss account?

(a) Overhead costs
(b) Direct costs
(c) Allowance for depreciation of assets
(d) Value of premises owned by the company
(e) Rent paid on occupied premises not owned by the company

Problems

1 Fig. 3.3 shows the costs of a firm in perfect competition in the short run. Assume profit maximization.

(i)   If the market price is OA how much will the firm produce?
(ii)   If the market price is OB how much will the firm produce?
(iii) If the market price is OC how much will the firm produce?
(iv)   If the market price is OD how much will the firm produce?
(v)   If the market price is OE how much will the firm produce?
(vi)   At what price will the firm make only normal profits?
(vii) At what price will the firm be on the point of shutting down in the short run?
(viii) At what price will the firm be of optimum size?
(ix)   How much profit in excess of normal will the firm make if price is OE?

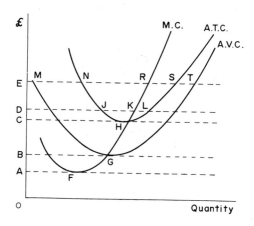

Fig. 3.3

2 The Wiesel Company has fixed costs of £60 and total costs as shown in the following table:

Output	Total costs			Average costs			Marginal costs
	Fixed	Variable	Total	Fixed	Variable	Total	
0	60	0	60	00	0	00	
1	60	50	110	60	50	110	50
2	60	80	140	30	40	70	30
3	60	105	165	20	35	55	25
4	60	152	212	15	38	53	47
5	60	225	285	12	45	57	68
6	60	330	390	10	55	65	105

(i)   Calculate the total fixed costs (T.F.C.), total variable costs (T.V.C.), average total costs (A.T.C.), average fixed costs (A.F.C.), average variable costs (A.V.C.), and marginal costs (M.C.) to complete the table.
(ii)   Plot the average and marginal curves on graph paper. (Plot the marginal values midway between the average — at output ½ to 5½ inclusive.)
(iii) Estimate from the graph A.T.C., A.V.C. and A.F.C. of producing 5½ units.
(iv)   Assume that the firm is operating under conditions of perfect competition and estimate from the graph:

(a) the maximum profit output if market price were £60
(b) the total profit (in excess of normal) in (a) above
(c) the market price at which the firm would be on the point of shutting down in the short run
(d) the quantity produced in (c) above
(e) the market price at which the firm would be making only normal profits

3 Fig. 3.4 shows the market situation of a monopolist.

    (i)   Which curve represents average fixed costs?
   (ii)   Which curve represents average total costs?
  (iii)   Which curve represents average variable costs?
   (iv)   Which curve represents marginal costs?
    (v)   Which curve represents marginal revenue?
   (vi)   Which curve represents total revenue?
  (vii)   Which curve represents average revenue?
 (viii)   Which curve represents total costs?
   (ix)   Which point indicates the minimum total cost position for the firm?
    (x)   Which point indicates the maximum profit position for the firm?
   (xi)   Which point indicates the output position for a firm trying to maximize sales without
          incurring losses?
  (xii)   Which curve is the monopolist's supply curve?

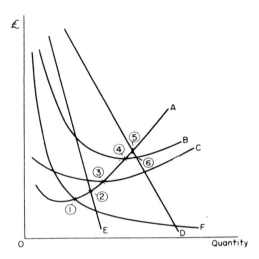

Fig. 3.4

$$\frac{TC}{Q} = \frac{Fe}{Q} + \frac{Ve}{Q}$$

4   A monopolist is faced with the market situation and costs shown in Fig. 3.5.

    (i)   What is his maximum profit output? *200*
   (ii) At what price will he sell output in (i) above? *60*
 (iii) What will be his total revenue in (i) above? *1200*
  (iv) What will be his total costs in (i) above? *6000*
   (v) How much monopoly profit will he make? *6000*
  (vi) If the monopolist were ordered to produce 300 units, how much would he get for each in the market? *60*
 (vii) How much monopoly profit would he get in (vi) above? *4500*
(viii) If the monopolist were faced with the same demand, but his average costs were constant at £60 per unit, what output would maximize his profits?
  (ix) At what price would he sell the output of (viii) above?
   (x) How much monopoly profit would he make in (viii) above?
  (xi) What is the elasticity of demand at a price of £40? *H*
 (xii) What is the elasticity of demand at a price of £60? *H*

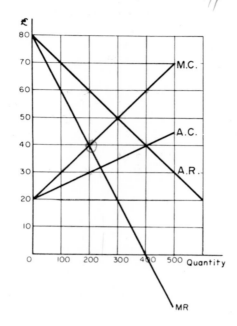

Fig. 3.5

5   The following table shows the marginal cost schedules (where they equal or exceed average costs) for three firms. Assume profit maximization and perfect competition.

Output	Marginal cost (£)		
	Firm I	Firm II	Firm III
0	0	0	0
1	15	40	65
2	20	50	70
3	25	60	75
4	30	70	80
5	35	80	85
6	40	90	90
7	45	100	95
8	50	110	100
9	55	120	105
10	60	130	110
11	65	140	115
12	70	150	120

  (i) At what price will firm I start producing? *15*
 (ii) At what price will firm II start producing? *40*
(iii) At what price will firm III start producing? *65*

(iv) Complete the supply schedule for the industry at the following prices:

Price (£)	0	10	20	30	40	50	60	70
Supply	0	0	2	4	7	10	13	18

 (v) All firms are price takers faced individually with horizontal demand curves. How much will the industry supply if market price is £60? *13*
 (vi) How much will firm I supply in (v) above? *10*
 (vii) How much will firm II supply in (v) above? *3*
 (viii) How much will firm III supply in (v) above? *0*
 (ix) What is the elasticity of supply for an increase in price from £50 to £60 in the industry? *+1½*
 (x) If a tax of £10 per unit is imposed, how much will the industry supply at a price of £60? *10*
 (xi) How much will firm I supply in (x) above? *8*
 (xii) How much will firm II supply in (x) above? *2*
 (xiii) How much will firm III supply in (x) above? *0*
 (xiv) If a subsidy of £10 per unit is paid to firms, how much will the industry supply at a price of £60?
 (xv) How much will firm I supply in (xiv) above? *12*
 (xvi) How much will firm II supply in (xiv) above? *4*
 (xvii) How much will firm III supply in (xiv) above? *2*

6 The following questions relate to the six diagrams in Fig. 3.6. Which of them illustrate

 (i) a firm in perfect competition making normal profits?
 (ii) a firm in perfect competition making supernormal profits in the short run?
 (iii) a natural monopoly?
 (iv) a monopolist making zero supernormal profits?
 (v) a monopolist making supernormal profits in the short run and losses in the long run?
 (vi) an oligopolist?

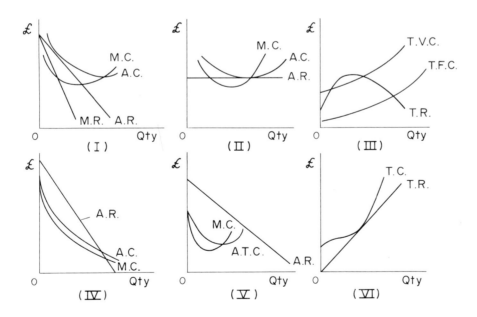

Fig. 3.6

7 Fig. 3.7 shows the total cost and revenue of a firm.

   (i)   In what kind of market does the firm operate? *Perfect competition*

  (ii)   What output maximizes profits? *O D*

 (iii)   What is the total profit (in excess of normal) earned in (ii) above? *L J*

  (iv)   What is the price at which the product is sold in (ii) above? *LD*

   (v)   What is the total of fixed costs in (ii) above? *ON* *OD*

  (vi)   At what output would the firm be making exactly normal profits? *B and O E*

 (vii)   At what output would the firm be making maximum losses? (Choose from the range in the diagram.) *O A*

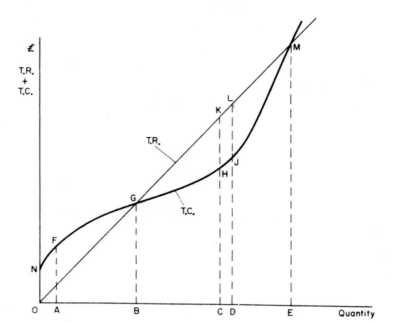

Fig. 3.7

8 Robert Palmer used to be a professional cricketer earning £15 000 a year. His wife, Margaret, has a part-time job working in her own home and earning £5 an hour. Robert has retired because of age. He has been offered work in a local factory at £6000 a year but has decided to buy a sweet-shop for £20 000. He raises this sum by borrowing £8000 from his father-in-law, who generously charges him only 5% interest, and £8000 from the bank, which charges him 15%. The remaining £4000 he has in his own savings, where it has been bringing him 10% interest per annum.

Last year Robert sold £25 000 worth of sweets which cost him £10 000 wholesale. He worked in the shop himself and employed a junior full-time assistant on an annual salary of £3000. His wife worked in the shop whenever needed. Last year she worked on average 4 hours a week for 50 weeks. His only other costs were rates (£250 per annum) and heat and light (£750 per annum). As it was the first year Robert and Margaret decided to live on their other savings so as not to take any money out of the business for themselves as they wanted to build it up.

   (i)   Looking at the business on a week-to-week basis, which are the variable costs?

  (ii)   What is the amount of their profit on an accounting basis?

 (iii)   What is the amount of their profit that would be recognized as such by an economist?

U.K. ECONOMY

Multiple Choice

Choose the alternative which provides the best answer to the question or completes the sentence most
satisfactorily.

1 Which of the following approximates most closely to the economic theory of (i) perfect competition,
(ii) oligopoly, (iii) monopolistic competition, (iv) monopoly?

(a) Detergents
(b) Dresses
(c) Greengrocery
(d) Wallpaper
(e) Two, or more, of the above

2 Approximately how many business enterprises produce nearly half of total manufacturing output in
the U.K.?

(a) 100
(b) 1000
(c) 10 000
(d) 100 000
(e) 200 000

3 Which of the following expanded most rapidly in the two decades before 1980?

(a) Wool textile exports
(b) Cotton textile production
(c) Wool textile production
(d) Cotton textile exports
(e) Man-made fibre production

4 In which of the following industries is the largest share of output produced by very large
business enterprises?

(a) Chemicals
(b) Clothing
(c) Furniture
(d) Leather goods
(e) Machine tools

5 Industrial concentration has tended to increase in Britain since the end of the Second World War,
partly as a result of amalgamations between firms. Which of the following kinds of merger have
been the most common cause of this?

(a) Conglomerate
(b) Diversified
(c) Horizontal
(d) Vertical
(e) All the above have been about the same.

6 Approximately what percentage of (i) the total number of workers and (ii) the total number of
establishments in manufacturing industry in Britain are employed in establishments with over 500
workers each?

(a) less than 5%
(b) 25%
(c) 50%
(d) 66%
(e) 75%

7 In which of the following industries are (i) the largest and (ii) the smallest proportions of
workers employed in very large establishments (plants)?

(a) Bricks
(b) Food
(c) Motor vehicles
(d) Textiles
(e) Timber

8 Which of the following types of retail business have increased their share of total trade most since the Second World War?

(a) Independents
(b) Multiples
(c) Department stores
(d) Co-operatives
(e) None of the above. All about the same.

9 What is the most important product by value of British farming?

(a) Cereals
(b) Eggs
(c) Fruit and vegetables
(d) Meat
(e) Milk

10 Which of the following industries are specialized (in the sense of having higher proportions of their labour forces than the national average) in the following regions of the U.K.: (i) South East England, (ii) East Anglia, (iii) Northern England, (iv) North West England and (v) West Midlands?

1. Chemicals
2. Finance
3. Food, drink and tobacco
4. Vehicles

(a) 1 only
(b) 2 only
(c) 3 only
(d) 4 only
(e) 1,3 and 4 only

11 Which of the following industries are (i) the most widely dispersed and (ii) the most highly localized?

1. Construction
2. Engineering
3. Food, drink and tobacco
4. Mining
5. Shipbuilding
6. Vehicles

(a) 2 and 5 only
(b) 1,2 and 3 only
(c) 1,3 and 4 only
(d) 4,5 and 6 only
(e) 1,4 and 6 only

12 Which of the following regions of the U.K. specialize (in the same sense as in question 10) in the following industries: (i) mining, (ii) iron and steel, (iii) shipbuilding, (iv) textiles, (v) transport?

1. South East England
2. South West England
3. The Midlands
4. North West England
5. Wales
6. Scotland

(a) 1 only
(b) 2 and 6 only
(c) 3 and 5 only
(d) 3,4 and 6 only
(e) 3,5 and 6 only

13 What proportion (approximate) of the labour force is employed in (i) the nationalized industries and (ii) the public sector as a whole?

   (a)   8%
   (b)   15%
   (c)   25%
   (d)   45%
   (e)   60%

14 The major sections of all but one of the following British industries are nationalized.   Which is the exception?

   (a)   Coal mining
   (b)   Gas distribution
   (c)   Road construction
   (d)   Rail transport
   (e)   Steel production

15 Nationalized industries in Britain have all the following characteristics with one exception. Which is the exception?

   (a)   They must publish annual accounts.
   (b)   They try to maximize their profits.
   (c)   They are set financial targets.
   (d)   They enjoy freedom from Parliament in the day-to-day operation of their business.
   (e)   They are not all absolute monopolies.

16 Which of the following industries has been nationalized twice since 1950?

   (a)   Coal
   (b)   Railways
   (c)   Motor cars
   (d)   Shipbuilding
   (e)   Steel

17 Which of the following has been the major change in the structure of the organization and control in British public companies since the 1960s?

   (a)   The appointment of Civil servants as directors
   (b)   The decline in the importance of shareholdings by financial institutions
   (c)   The decline in the importance of take-over bids
   (d)   The decline in the use of proxy votes
   (e)   The decline in the importance of personal shareholdings

18 A (i) public company and (ii) public corporation is

   (a)   one which operates in the public sector of the economy.
   (b)   one which is owned and controlled by members of the public who buy its products.
   (c)   one whose liabilities to the public are carried without limit by shareholders.
   (d)   one which is owned by private individuals.
   (e)   one with over 50 shareholders.

Exercises

Note: Sources are suggested for all exercises. Alternatives may be available if the one mentioned is not in your library. For advice on them and on the collection and presentation of data in tabular and graphical form see pp. ix-x.

1 Complete columns (i) to (iii) of the following table with figures of the Index of Industrial Production for a recent year and for 5 and 10 years previously. Divide the index numbers for each of the last two years by that for the earliest year for each industry to show in columns (iv) and (v) the percentage increases that have taken place since then.

Industry	Year 19.... (i)	19.... (ii)	19.... (iii)	Index numbers 19.... = 100 (iv)	19.... = 100 (v)
Mining and quarrying					
Food, drink and tobacco					
Chemicals					
Metal manufacture					
Engineering					
Shipbuilding					
Vehicles					
Textiles					
Bricks, etc.					
Timber, furniture, etc.					
Paper, printing, etc.					
Construction					
ALL INDUSTRIES					

Source: Annual Abstract of Statistics

   (i)   Which industries expanded more than and less than the total for all industries?
  (ii)   What explanation can you offer for the changes noted in (i) above?
 (iii)   How do the changes over the 10 years in the table compare with long-term trends since the beginning of the century?
  (iv)   Do you consider that the recent trends are likely to continue over the next 10 years? (A graph might help you here.)

2 In the Summary Tables volume of the Census of Production for a recent year you should find two sets of tables grouping industries according to the numbers of workers in (1) establishments and (2) enterprises of different size. Extract the data necessary to complete the following tables, calculating also the percentages of the total numbers of workers in each size class for all industries.

ESTABLISHMENTS

Industry	Number of workers Less than 100 No.	%	100-1499 No.	%	1500 and over No.	%	Total No.	%
Bricks, cement etc.								100
Chemicals								100
Clothing and footwear								100
Electrical engineering								100
Food, drink and tobacco								100
Mechanical engineering								100
Metal manufacture								100
Textiles								100
Vehicles								100
ALL MANUFACTURING								100

ENTERPRISES

Industry	Number of workers						Total	
	Less than 1000		1000–19 999		20 000 and over			
	No.	%	No.	%	No.	%	No.	%
Bricks, cement, etc.								100
Chemicals								100
Clothing and footwear								100
Electrical engineering								100
Food, drink and tobacco								100
Mechanical engineering								100
Metal manufacture								100
Textiles								100
Vehicles								100
ALL MANUFACTURING								100

Source: Census of Production 19....

  (i)   What is the difference between an establishment and an enterprise?
 (ii)   Which of the industries in the tables are the most and the least highly concentrated in (a)
         large establishments and (b) large enterprises?
(iii)   Which of the two tables provides the better evidence of the prevalence of economies of
         large-scale production in British industry and why?
 (iv)   Which of the two tables provides the better evidence of the prevalence of monopoly power in
         British industry and why?
  (v)   What additional information would help you to assess the extent of monopoly power in an
         industry?

3 From Who Owns Whom in your local reference library find ten companies which have subsidiaries of
       subsidiaries, and three companies which have subsidiaries of subsidiaries of subsidiaries. Can
       you find a company which has subsidiaries of subsidiaries of subsidiaries of subsidiaries?
       Prepare a 'family tree' for a company with at least three 'levels' of subsidiaries. Find the
       address of the registered office of the principal (holding) company and write for a copy of its
       latest annual report and accounts.

  (i)   Can you classify the company as being horizontally or vertically integrated, or is it a
         conglomerate?
 (ii)   Did the group of companies expand or contract last year? If so was it primarily by
         internal growth or by the acquisition of outside subsidiaries?
(iii)   How far can you say whether the group possesses monopoly power in any of its markets.
         Does it possess any monopsony power?
 (iv)   If the group acquired any new companies last year, what effect do you think this had on
         (a) its costs of production and (b) its market power?

4   From the <u>Annual Abstract of Statistics</u> extract information on the net output and the numbers of employees recorded in two Censuses of Production for a recent year and for another about ten years previously for the industries in the following table. Calculate the percentage changes in output and employment between the two years for each industry.

	Numbers of employees 19... | 19...	% Change 19... to 19...	Net output 19... | 19...	% Change 19... to 19...
Food, drink and tobacco				
Chemicals				
Metal manufacture				
Engineering				
Textiles and clothing				
Mining				
Construction				
All manufacturing industries				
All Census industries				

Source: Annual Abstract of Statistics

  (i)   What is the difference between the total for manufacturing and for all Census industries? Can you find any industries which are not in either total?
 (ii)   Rank the industries by size of (a) net output and (b) numbers of employees in the most recent year. Compare the rankings and offer explanations for such differences as you find. What additional information might help you provide better explanations?
(iii)   Which industries (a) expanded and (b) contracted <u>relative</u> to the average for all industries between the two years? Do you think the reasons for their different relative progress are to be found mainly in supply or demand factors in individual cases?

5   <u>The Times</u> newspaper has an annual publication called <u>The Times 1000</u> which ranks the largest companies in Britain according to the values of their sales turnover. Complete the following table from the information contained there, calculating the percentages of total capital employed, total profits, and total numbers of employees of the largest 100 companies for each size bracket shown. Does the use of the three different measures of size affect the proportions in columns (ii), (iv) and (vi)? If so, can you say why?

Rank order of companies	Capital employed £,000m (i)	% (ii)	Profit pre-tax £m (iii)	% (iv)	Numbers of employees Nos (v)	% (vi)
1 - 10						
11 - 24						
25 - 49						
50 - 74						
75 - 100						
Top 100		100%		100%		100%

Source: The Times 1000

Compare the total profits of these companies with the total income of all U.K. companies in the private sector in the same year. (Source: <u>National Income and Expenditure.</u>) How important are these large companies on the national scale? Repeat this last exercise for an earlier year (preferably one several years ago) and compare your results. Note the average rates of return on capital for the different size groups of companies in the 'Top 1000'. Do they suggest that the very largest companies are more or less profitable than relatively smaller ones. Can you think of any market forces which might prevent any conclusions being drawn on this matter from this kind of evidence?

6   Find out the price charged for men's haircuts at 6 local barbers. Find also the price of a table d'hôte lunch at 6 local restaurants. What, if anything, does the evidence you have found suggest about types of market for these two service industries?

7 Using data from the <u>Annual Abstract of Statistics</u> prepare a graph showing the course of trade of the following types of retail business over the last 5 years:

> Independent retailers
> Multiple retailers
> Co-operative societies

(i) Rank them according to their growth rates. Do the results suggest that concentration has been increasing or diminishing?

(ii) Why do you think they may have grown at different rates? Do you regard the trends as indicating an improvement in the efficiency of retail trading?

(iii) Refer now to the statistical breakdown in the <u>Annual Abstract of Statistics</u> for (a) food, (b) clothing and footwear, and (c) durable house-hold goods. Are the growth rankings the same for independents, multiples and co-operatives in all three sectors? If not, can you say why?

8 From the Yellow Pages of the local telephone directory or of Kelly's Directory, draw a sample of the first 10 firms alphabetically in 6 different trades or businesses and determine the proportion of joint-stock companies to other firms in each industry. Which have the highest and lowest proportions as companies? Can you suggest reasons why this is so? How far do you think you might have reached different results if you had been able to collect data relating to the turnover of the businesses in your samples?

9 Extract data from the <u>Annual Abstract of Statistics</u> on the income and finance of 'listed companies' to complete the following table on sources of funds for a recent year and for two others, 5 and 10 years ago. Calculate the percentages of the totals for each year.

	Year 19....		Year 19....		Year 19....	
	£m	%	£m	%	£m	%
Issues of shares for cash Ordinary shares						
Preference shares						
Long-term loans						
Total						
Issues of shares in exchange for subsidiaries						
Increases in borrowing from banks and trade creditors						
TOTAL of the above		100%		100%		100%

Source: Annual Abstract of Statistics

(i) What are 'listed companies'?

(ii) Which are the most important kind of shares (in terms of value) issued for cash in each year?

(iii) What trends have occurred in the relative importance of cash issues, acquisitions of subsidiaries and borrowing from banks and trade creditors? Which of them is the best indicator of the level of industrial concentration in industry over time? If none are good indicators, why is this so?

10 Using data from the <u>Annual Abstract of Statistics</u> prepare a graph showing the numbers of companies acquired as a result of mergers and total expenditure on acquisitions over the last 5 to 10 years. Does it show any evidence of a merger 'wave'? Would you regard an increase in amalgamations between companies as contributing to or subtracting from the efficiency of the economy? What additional information about <u>types</u> of merger might help you answer the last question?

11 Obtain a copy of the trading and profit and loss accounts of the National Coal Board and one of the Regional Electricity Boards for a recent year. Make judgements about whether the main expenditure items are fixed or variable costs. Compare the proportions of fixed to variable costs in the two industries. (Ignore any items which are quite impossible to judge.) What difference in the proportions would you expect if the basis of the accounts was 5 years? Should any differences you find influence the pricing policies of the two industries?

12 On your next visit to a local factory, try and find out some of the following: whether it is an independent company or a subsidiary; whether it sets the price of its product or takes market price as given; whether it spends a lot on advertising; whether the unit costs of its main line of product tend to rise, fall or remain constant. From the information you get on any of these points, try to assess the type of market situation facing the firm.

Essays

1. What characteristics must a market possess in order that it should be described as 'perfect'? Are there any British industries which come near to being so described?

2. What factors determine the cost curves of a firm in the short run and in the long run?

3. Distinguish between internal and external economies of scale. Are either compatible with perfect competition?

4. Show that the factors which influence the maximum profit position of a firm differ from those which determine whether or not it should shut down.

5. Show how to derive the long-run cost curves for a firm from its short-run cost curves.

6. Explain the relationship between the supply curve for an industry and the cost curves of individual firms.

7. What explanations can be given for cost curves being U-shaped and L-shaped?

8. Under what conditions would a firm produce at the minimum point on its average cost curve?

9. Is the existence of a single uniform price in an industry evidence of perfect competition or imperfect competition?

10. A monopolist owner of a natural beauty spot is assumed to incur no variable costs when he offers to let people view it. If he wants to maximize his profits what price should he charge and how many people should he let in?

11. 'A profit-maximizing monopolist always operates on the downward-sloping portion of his average cost curve. In perfectly competitive markets no firm ever does so.' Discuss.

12. 'The more narrowly an industry is defined the greater the degree of apparent monopoly, but the less monopoly power it possesses because of the larger number of substitutes that are likely to exist.' Explain and comment.

13. 'In perfect competition all firms earn normal profits. Under monopoly they all earn supernormal profits.' Discuss.

14. Are big firms likely to be more monopolistic than small ones? Illustrate your answer by reference to British industry.

15. 'All monopoly power rests fundamentally on the existence of barriers to entry.' Discuss.

16. How far can the profitability of a firm be taken as a guide to its efficiency?

17. What are the main differences between the theory of oligopoly and that of monopolistic competition?

18. Distinguish between vertical integration, horizontal integration and conglomerate mergers. Explain the main ways in which firms may undertake each.

19. Explain why a firm may be in equilibrium while the industry is not. Can the industry be in equilibrium while a firm is not?

20. Explain the effects of advertising expenditure on a firm's cost and demand curves.

21. Describe the main ways in which firms can raise capital for expansion.

22. What relationship is there between the distribution of share ownership and the goals pursued by a firm?

23. What are the main advantages and disadvantages of the joint-stock form of business organization?

24. Distinguish between the motives that can lead to a merger between two firms in an industry.

25. How useful do you consider the statement that the chief difference between public and private enterprise is whether the main object is the maximizing of profits?

26. Under what conditions does it pay a firm to sell its products at different prices to different consumers?

CHAPTER 4

Distribution: Factors of Production and their Prices

The study of factors of production plays a double role in economics. It helps to answer two of the main questions referred to at the beginning of this book: (1) how production is best organized (because factor prices and productivities lie behind the cost curves of firms) and (2) for whom goods are produced (because the prices of factors of production lie behind the distribution of incomes).

Market determination of the prices of factors of production, labour, capital and land, is analysed in a manner closely paralleling that used for the prices of goods and services — by studying the forces of supply and demand.

DEMAND   The demand for the services of a factor of production is the schedule of quantities which businesses want to buy at varying prices during a period of time. The demand is said to be DERIVED from the value of the goods which a factor produces. It is determined by a factor's productivity and the ease with which it may be substituted for other factors. The elasticity of demand for a factor depends on these influences, on the time allowed for a price change to take effect and on the relative importance of the factor in total costs.

The technical efficiency, or productivity, with which factors of production can be combined to produce given outputs (the PRODUCTION FUNCTION) is a basic determinant of the costs of a firm. When the prices of the services of factors are known, a firm is able to select the least cost combination for each level of output. Productivity depends critically upon whether the short period or the long period is under consideration. The short period is defined as that during which at least one of the factors is fixed in supply. As units of a VARIABLE factor are used together with a fixed one, the MARGINAL PHYSICAL PRODUCT (M.P.P.) of the variable factor tends eventually to fall. This phenomenon is known as the LAW OF DIMINISHING RETURNS. It is attributed to the increasing difficulty of substitution with changing proportions as the fixed factor becomes scarce. The demand for a factor of production is the M.P.P. multiplied by the marginal revenue to the firm of the extra output — the MARGINAL REVENUE PRODUCT (M.R.P.). The quantity of a factor purchased by a firm depends, therefore, on its productivity and cost. A profit-maximizing firm will be in equilibrium for the production of a given output when the marginal revenue product of each factor is equal to the marginal cost of the factor. The least cost combination of inputs of two factors, A and B, is where $\dfrac{\text{M.R.P.}_A}{\text{M.C.}_A} = \dfrac{\text{M.R.P.}_B}{\text{M.C.}_B}$. In conditions of perfect competition, when a firm is considered in isolation, M.R.P. is the same as M.P.P. multiplied by the price of the product (the VALUE OF THE MARGINAL PRODUCT, V.M.P.). When a firm is a monopolist in the market for its product, M.R. is less than price and M.R.P. is accordingly below V.M.P. When, however, a firm exerts monopoly power in the factor market, so that the price of a factor which it uses is affected by the quantity it buys, it is called a MONOPSONIST (single buyer) and the marginal cost of the factor is greater than its price. In the long run all factors can be varied, and there is no need for the proportions in which they are used to be changed. Productivity depends then on the SCALE OF PRODUCTION. If a percentage change in the quantity of all factors causes a smaller, equal or larger percentage change in total output, there are said to be DECREASING, CONSTANT or INCREASING RETURNS TO SCALE respectively.

SUPPLY   It is more difficult to generalize about the determinants of the supply of productive services than about the demand for them. Institutional considerations become highly relevant and it is usual to deal separately with the price of each of the main productive factors.

WAGES are the price of LABOUR. It is sometimes useful to assume initially that all labour is HOMOGENEOUS, equally skilled and equally efficient, so that, whatever the nature of the supply curve of labour, forces of competition would act to equalize the wages in all occupations, subject only to the fact that some jobs are more disagreeable than others. The NON-PECUNIARY ADVANTAGES and DISADVANTAGES of individual occupations would account for premium and discount rates for them. But the assumption of homogeneity is clearly unrealistic and the idea of NON-COMPETING GROUPS is introduced to distinguish markets for different qualities and types of labour.

The relevant supply curve for the analysis of wages is, then, that for a particular kind of labour. It may be the supply of labour with a special skill in a particular occupation or industry or in a specific region. Behind a particular supply curve lies the notion of MOBILITY OF LABOUR, which may reflect the costs of movement from place to place, search costs involved in looking around for work and the costs of training to acquire skills (sometimes referred to as investment in HUMAN CAPITAL).

When considering a supply curve of labour, units of measurement must be clearly stated, e.g. whether the quantity axis measures hours of work or numbers of workers. The former is probably best used for the analysis of the reactions of an individual to a wage rate change. It may be shown that an increase in the wage rate, for instance, may lead to either an increase or a reduction in effort; for a rise in wages has both an income and a substitution effect. As a person finds his real income has risen he may want more leisure in which to enjoy it, and this may more than offset the substitution effect of the wage increase, which makes work more attractive.

The number of workers offering their services at varying wage rates can be approached at two levels, taking the population as given and allowing for changes in the size of the labour force. The first is a short-run situation. For the analysis of wages in a given industry, the derived demand for labour at different rates of pay is put together with the appropriate supply of labour, reflecting any training costs, non-pecuniary disadvantages, etc. The degree of competition on the supply side must also be considered. In modern industrial societies competition is affected by the existence of TRADE UNIONS, which may influence wage rates by controlling supply. Collective bargaining takes many forms and is concerned with wages, hours and other conditions of work. It may even influence the demand for labour as well as the supply if productivity rises (e.g. by substitution of piece rates for time rates, or vice versa).

In the LONG RUN the supply of labour depends on the size of the POPULATION itself. The general level of wages, therefore, reflects, to some extent, the scarcity of labour relative to other factors of production. Changes in the population depend upon three main factors: the BIRTH-RATES, DEATH-RATES and NET MIGRATION. The last of these is largely a political matter; death-rates are linked to medical advance and living standards, while birth-rates depend upon the number of marriages and family-size habits. The size of the LABOUR FORCE (or WORKING POPULATION) in a given population is mainly a matter of age distribution, the proportion who are neither too old nor too young for work. In its turn this variable depends upon the school-leaving age, the age of retirement and such social matters as the proportion of married women who work. The supply of labour in an area is also affected by the regional distribution of the labour force, which, though historically based, is open to influence by government policy.

RENT is the name traditionally given to the return for the use of LAND. This factor was originally singled out by Ricardo because land is fixed in supply. Today, rent is recognized to have limited applicability to land prices because of the alternative uses to which land can be put. At the same time ECONOMIC RENT can apply to any factor of production the supply of which is fixed and which has only a single use, implying zero opportunity costs. No price need be paid to secure its employment. Any such income is therefore a surplus (the producers' counterpart of consumers' surplus) and does not enter into the real costs of production. Generally, if a factor is not in perfectly elastic supply some part of its income is in excess of its opportunity cost, or TRANSFER EARNINGS, and is economic rent. Factors of production which earn surpluses in the short run only are paid QUASI-RENTS.

PROFIT is the term used to describe a number of different types of income. In one sense it is the reward for undertaking certain types of unpredictable or uninsurable risks, called uncertainties, or it may be regarded as a return for innovating, applying new techniques which help economic development. In both cases it is the expectation of profit that performs the important economic function. Profits are also used to refer to the earnings arising from the existence of monopoly power. The residual after subtracting total costs from total revenue is a firm's profit, but accounting profits may differ from profits in an economic sense if all costs are not valued in real opportunity cost terms. Profits are usually expressed as percentage rates of return of the value of the assets of a business for comparative purposes. NORMAL PROFIT is the minimum a firm must earn to keep it in an industry.

INTEREST is the return to the factor of production CAPITAL. The theory of interest rates is a difficult subject and treatment is often delayed beyond an introductory course in economics. It is also hard to find the best place to treat the subject since the factors behind supply and demand which determine the market rate of interest are of two kinds, real and monetary. The monetary forces are best left until the nature of money and banks have been dealt with, while the real factors by themselves are only one side of the picture.

Interest, usually discussed as a rate per cent, is paid for the present use of money in the market for loans, or loanable funds. It is the price which is paid by borrowers and received by lenders. The demand for loanable funds can come from persons wishing to consume more than their income, e.g. to buy a durable asset like a house. But the main element in demand is usually from businesses which are contemplating the production of goods by more capitalistic, or ROUNDABOUT, means involving, for example, the purchase of machinery. The introduction of such production methods involves a time lag between the outlay and receipt of the revenues which eventually accrue over a machine's life. Capital is needed to cover this time lag. Businesses may be considered to be faced with a range of potential schemes of varying productivity, and a downward-sloping demand curve representing the MARGINAL PRODUCTIVITY (or EFFICIENCY) OF CAPITAL may be assumed as a first approximation. The cost of capital is the rate of interest that must be paid for it (or its opportunity cost). When the marginal revenue product of an investment project exceeds its cost, then it is worth undertaking. Assessment of the profitability of investment can also be made by calculating the PRESENT VALUE of a stream of future incomes accruing from a capital outlay, using standard compound interest formulae. The supply of loanable funds can include the savings of persons who forego present consumption in return for consumption in the future. Since there is a TIME PREFERENCE for present rather than future consumption, the rate of interest which must be paid might be expected to be positive, to induce the individual to abstain from present consumption. Savings are not, however, determined by the rate of interest alone and the supply and demand for loanable funds is affected by many institutional and monetary factors including the demand for and supply of money itself, the general level of prices and the availability of credit. These matters are dealt with in the following two chapters.

In conclusion it should be added that the distribution of <u>factor</u> incomes depends on the price of each factor of production. The distribution of <u>personal</u> incomes is determined by these same factor prices but also by the distribution of factor endowments, which establish how much each individual receives as wages, rent, interest and profit.

ANALYSIS

Multiple Choice

Choose the alternative which provides the best answer to the question or completes the sentence most satisfactorily.

1 The demand for labour as a factor of production is said to be a derived demand because

   (a) labour is always used in conjunction with at least one other factor of production.
   (b) labour is only required because it is productive.
   (c) labour demand also depends on labour supply.
   (d) labour demand depends indirectly on how much workers value leisure time.
   (e) no one demands labour unless they have cash to pay wages.

2 Which of the following would tend to make labour mobility relatively low?

   (a) Most skills are easily acquired.
   (b) Workers have a fund of savings to tide them over periods of unemployment.
   (c) There are few non-pecuniary advantages attaching to most occupations.
   (d) Because of monopoly in most industries workers are paid less than the value of their marginal product.
   (e) There is a general housing shortage.

3

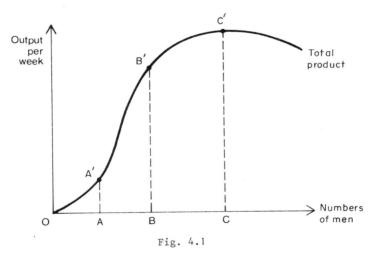

Fig. 4.1

Fig. 4.1 shows the maximum output obtainable by employing varying numbers of men in combination with a fixed quantity of capital in a factory. Which of the following statements is correct?

   (a) Marginal product is equal to average product when OB men are employed.
   (b) The 'law' of diminishing returns starts to operate after OC men are employed.
   (c) Average product is at a maximum when OC men are employed.
   (d) Increasing returns to scale operate until OA men are employed.
   (e) Average product exceeds marginal product when between OB and OC men are employed.

4 If a firm's employment of factors is such that the law of diminishing returns is operating

   (a) all factors of production must be variable.
   (b) factors of production must be used in fixed proportions.
   (c) at least two factors of production must be variable.
   (d) one or more factors of production must be fixed.
   (e) the demand for the industry's product must be inelastic.

5 The following data relate to the outputs corresponding to certain combinations of inputs used in a firm. Which of the following are illustrated by the figures:

Inputs		Output
Capital	Labour	
1	1	10
1	2	16
1	3	22
2	1	15
2	2	20
3	1	18

(a) Diminishing returns to labour
(b) Increasing returns to capital
(c) Decreasing returns to scale
(d) Increasing returns to scale
(e) None of the above

6 Demand for a factor of production depends upon all the following except

(a) the degree to which it may be substituted for other factors.
(b) the demand for the product.
(c) the marginal (revenue) product of the factor.
(d) the size of the labour force.
(e) whether the short period or the long period is being considered.

7 The marginal productivity theory of wages states that

(a) wages are determined by the marginal physical product of labour.
(b) wages are such as to equalize the marginal physical product of labour and its supply.
(c) the demand for labour is determined by the marginal physical product of labour multiplied by its marginal revenue.
(d) labour receives a wage equal to its marginal physical product.
(e) labour receives a wage equal to the value of its marginal product.

8 The elasticity of demand for labour will tend to be high if

(a) the elasticity of supply of labour is also high.
(b) the elasticity of demand for the product is also high.
(c) non-labour costs are a high proportion of total costs.
(d) labour is an essential input as it cannot easily be replaced by other factors of production.
(e) one is concerned with the short run rather than the long run.

9 A firm which is a monopsonist in the market for its labour will find that

(a) it must lower the price of its product if it is to sell more of it.
(b) it must raise the wage rate if it employs more labour.
(c) the wage rate is not affected by the supply of labour.
(d) the wage rate tends to fall as more men are employed.
(e) the supply of labour is perfectly inelastic.

10 If boys follow the occupations of their fathers, this will be most likely to

(a) reduce the mobility of labour.
(b) raise the elasticity of demand for labour.
(c) lower the non-pecuniary advantages of some trades.
(d) lower the general level of wage rates.
(e) increase the elasticity of supply of labour.

11 The supply schedule of labour is dependent on all the following except the

(a) degree of mobility of labour.
(b) costs of training.
(c) marginal (revenue) product of labour.
(d) strength of trade unions.
(e) size of the population.

12 If there is a rise in wage rates and men are induced to work fewer hours, this means that

(a) the supply curve of labour slopes downwards to the right.
(b) men prefer work to leisure at the margin.
(c) men prefer leisure to work.
(d) the substitution effect of the change in wage rates more than offsets the income effect.
(e) men actually enjoy their work.

13

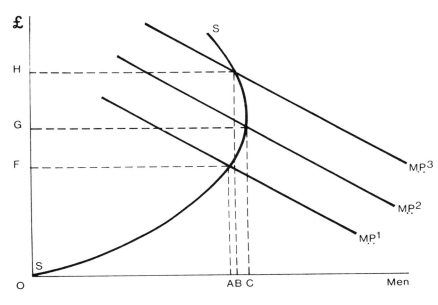

Fig. 4.2

Fig. 4.2 shows the marginal product of labour working with a fixed quantity of other factors in a perfectly competitive industry. $M.P.^1$, $M.P.^2$ and $M.P.^3$ refer to the original situation and that after each of two productivity increases. SS is the supply curve of labour to the industry and is assumed to remain unchanged throughout. Which of the following statements is correct?

(a) Employment rises most after the second productivity change.
(b) Employment falls least after the first productivity change.
(c) Wage rates rise most after the first productivity change.
(d) The maximum wage that the industry can pay occurs after the second productivity increase.
(e) The maximum employment that the industry can sustain occurs after the first productivity increase.

14 The value of the marginal product of labour differs from the marginal revenue product of labour when there is

(a) perfect competition in the labour market.
(b) imperfect competition in the labour market.
(c) perfect competition in the product market.
(d) imperfect competition in the product market.
(e) None of the above is correct.

15 The table below shows the total weekly output of plates obtainable by a firm in perfect competition as a result of varying the amount of labour it employs with a fixed quantity of capital. Plates sell at 40p each and the firm employs 4 men in equilibrium. What is the weekly wage rate?

Number of men	Total output of plates
1	2000
2	2500
3	2900
4	3000
5	3100
6	3150

(a) £20   (d) £40
(b) £25   (e) £50
(c) £30

16 The imposition of a legal minimum wage rate above market equilibrium in a perfectly competitive labour market (i) will have <u>no</u> effect on the level of employment and (ii) will <u>not</u> succeed in raising the wage rate for workers remaining in employment

    (a) if the elasticity of demand for labour is zero.
    (b) if the elasticity of demand for labour is infinity.
    (c) if the elasticity of supply of labour is zero.
    (d) if the elasticity of supply of labour is infinity.
    (e) None of the above.

17 A business decides to increase its purchases of a raw material from 10 to 11 tonnes. In order to do so it has to pay £1050 per tonne instead of £1000 per tonne. What is the marginal cost (per tonne) to the business?

    (a) £50
    (b) £500
    (c) £550
    (d) £1050
    (e) £1550

18 A firm uses two factors of production capital (K) and labour (L), the prices of which are not affected by the quantities used by the firm. Which of the following equalities describes its best combination of inputs? (Note: M.R.P. stands for marginal revenue product, V.M.P. stands for value of the marginal product and P stands for the price of the factor.)

    (a) $\text{M.R.P.}_K = \text{M.R.P.}_L$

    (b) $\text{V.M.P.}_K = \text{V.M.P.}_L$

    (c) $\text{V.M.P.}_K \times P_K = \text{V.M.P.}_L \times P_L$

    (d) $\dfrac{\text{V.M.P.}_K}{P_K} = \dfrac{\text{V.M.P.}_L}{P_L}$

    (e) $\dfrac{\text{M.R.P.}_K}{P_K} = \dfrac{\text{M.R.P.}_L}{P_L}$

19 From the following list of assumptions, select those which help to make it likely that money wage rates will be the same in all occupations.

    1. No individual employer can affect the price of labour by varying the quantity he employs.
    2. Mobility of labour is perfect and costless.
    3. The non-pecuniary advantages of different occupations vary inversely and in proportion to wage rates in them.
    4. No monopoly exists in the market for the product of any industry.
    5. All men are equally productive.
    6. All jobs are equally attractive.

    (a) 2,5 and 6 only
    (b) 1,3,4 and 5 only
    (c) 1,2,4 and 6 only
    (d) 2,4,5 and 6 only
    (e) 1,2,5 and 6 only

20 The following reasons have been put forward at one time or another to explain the fact that women's wages have tended to be lower than men's. (i) Which of them relate principally to the supply of women's labour rather than to the demand for it? (ii) Which of them might explain why women's wages were <u>higher</u> than men's?

    1. A man needs more to support a family.
    2. Married women have domestic responsibilities which make work less attractive.
    3. Women have higher absence rates.
    4. Women leave work to get married.
    5. Women are physically weaker.
    6. Women tend to have less vocational training.
    7. Fewer women join trade unions.

	(i)		(ii)
(a)	1 and 5 only	(a)	1 only
(b)	2 and 7 only	(b)	2 only
(c)	4,5 and 6 only	(c)	3,4 and 5 only
(d)	1,2 and 7 only	(d)	6 only
(e)	2,3 and 4 only	(e)	7 only.

21 A trade union succeeds in raising wage rates at the cost of some unemployment in a market where employers have no monopsony power. The extra earnings of those remaining in employment would be enough to compensate fully the lost earnings of those who lose their jobs if

(a) the elasticity of supply of labour is equal to or less than unity.
(b) the elasticity of supply of labour is equal to or greater than unity.
(c) the elasticity of demand for labour is equal to or less than unity.
(d) the elasticity of demand for labour is equal to or greater than unity.
(e) both the elasticity of demand and supply of labour are equal to unity.

22 A trade union will be more likely to succeed in raising the wages of its members without causing unemployment if

(a) it can control the supply of labour.
(b) the industry is in the hands of a monopoly.
(c) it is dealing with a monopsony employer.
(d) productivity is increased.
(e) there are no alternative industries in which its labour force might be employed.

23 The size of the national labour force in a population of given size depends least on the

(a) age distribution of the population.
(b) general level of wages.
(c) school-leaving age.
(d) location of industry.
(e) normal retiring age.

24 Predictions of the size of each of the following items for 10 years ahead are called for. Which is likeky to be least reliable? (Assume no wars, catastrophes or net migration.)

(a) The total population
(b) The number of women of child-bearing age alive at the time
(c) The number of births during the year
(d) The proportion of men to women in the population
(e) The number of deaths in the 20-30 age group

25 Malthus's theory of population has been mainly criticized on the grounds that he

(a) did not appreciate that there would be a decline in the death-rate with medical advance.
(b) did not foresee the growth of the trade union movement.
(c) thought that the total quantity of land in the world would remain fixed.
(d) did not appreciate the extent to which techniques of production would alter.
(e) did not know of any means of controlling the birth-rate.

26 Land is said to earn economic rent if

(a) the supply of land is fixed.
(b) land is in perfectly elastic supply.
(c) land has only a single use.
(d) the demand for land is perfectly elastic.
(e) the productivity of land cannot be raised.

27 A singer could earn £100 a week as a clerk, £150 a week in a factory, £200 a week as an insurance salesman, but in fact earns £500 a week as a singer. Her economic rent is

(a) zero.
(b) £300.
(c) £350.
(d) £400.
(e) £500.

28 Transfer earnings received by a factor of production are another name for

(a) the economic rent received by the factor.
(b) the difference between the economic rent and the opportunity cost of the factor.
(c) the cost of substituting one factor for another.
(d) the cost of transferring from one industry to another.
(e) the minimum compensation that must be paid to persuade a factor to move from one industry to another.

29

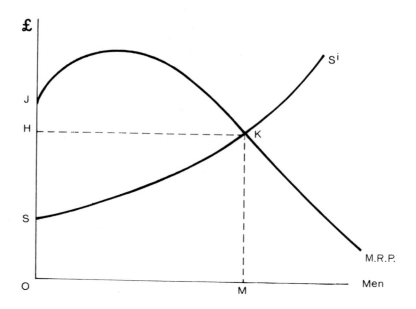

Fig. 4.3

Fig. 4.3 shows the supply curve of labour and its marginal revenue product. All workers are assumed to be paid the equilibrium market wage. Economic rent earned by the workers in the industry is given by the area

(a) SKH.
(b) OSKM.
(c) HJK.
(d) SKJ.
(e) OHKM.

30 A tax on a factor of production which receives an income consisting solely of economic rent

(a) will be passed on to consumers regardless of the elasticity of demand.
(b) will be borne by the factor regardless of the elasticity of demand.
(c) will be passed on to buyers of the factor if demand is inelastic.
(d) will be borne by the factor if demand is elastic.
(e) may be borne in part by the factor and in part by buyers of the factor depending on the elasticity of demand.

31 A firm buys a machine expecting it will yield 15% return for 2 years, after which it will be worn out and need replacing. It actually yields 20% because demand increased immediately after the machine was installed. An economist would regard the difference between the 15% and 20% as consisting of

(a) pure profit.
(b) pure economic rent.
(c) quasi-rent.
(d) part quasi-rent.
(e) part rent and part profit.

32 A market rate of interest of 10% implies that

(a) people prefer £10 now to £100 next year.
(b) the average yield on capital is 10%.
(c) 95% of the national income is used for present consumption.
(d) the marginal productivity of capital is 10%.
(e) everybody prefers £110 next year to £100 now.

33 An investment project will be worth while if

(a) the sum of its future income yields is greater than the cost of the project.
(b) the rate of interest is greater than the rate of return on the investment.
(c) the discounted present value of the stream of future yields is greater than the cost of the project.
(d) the future yields are greater than those obtainable in any other investment project.
(e) All of the above are correct.

34 The marginal efficiency of capital tends to be greater

  (a) the larger the stock of capital already invested.
  (b) the more rapid the rate of technical advance.
  (c) the higher the marginal productivity of labour and other factors of production.
  (d) the higher the rate of interest.
  (e) All of the above are correct.

35 The present value of a future stream of income resulting from a sum of money invested will be higher

  (a) the longer the waiting period between investment and receipt of income.
  (b) the higher the rate of interest.
  (c) the smaller the sum invested.
  (d) the greater the number of other factors of production needed.
  (e) None of the above.

36 £100 lent at 5% compound interest will in 15 years' time be worth approximately

  (a) £208.
  (b) £183.
  (c) £175.
  (d) £167.
  (e) £150.

37 The present value of an investment of £500 yielding £1000 in one year's time when the rate of interest is 25% is

  (a) £625.
  (b) £750.
  (c) £800.
  (d) £1000.
  (e) £1250.

38 When economists refer to investment in human capital, they mean

  (a) the employment of expert professional workers.
  (b) expenditure on education and training.
  (c) the purchase of slaves.
  (d) immigration of workers.
  (e) Any of the above.

39 To an economist, profits are

  (a) the difference between total costs and total receipts.
  (b) a reward for risk-taking.
  (c) a reward for innovations.
  (d) unforeseen yields on investment.
  (e) Any of the above.

Problems

1   Fig. 4.4 shows the supply (SS) and demand for labour working with a fixed quantity of capital in a market where there are no monopoly elements and profit maximization is assumed.

    (i)   What is the equilibrium level of employment?
    (ii)   What is the equilibrium wage rate?
   (iii)   What is the total wage bill?
    (iv)   What is the total product of labour?
    (v)   What are the total receipts of capital?
    (vi)   A trade union is now formed which has the effect of shifting the supply curve of labour to S'S'. What is the new equilibrium wage rate?
   (vii)   What is the change in the level of employment?
  (viii)   If the union had succeeded in restricting the number of workers in the industry to OE, what wage rate could it have secured?
    (ix)   What is the difference in total wages received by all workers after the restriction of supply to OE, compared with the original situation?
    (x)   Under what conditions would the total wage bill have increased in (ix) above?
    (xi)   If the union were determined to get a wage of OB without a reduction in total employment, and it could negotiate an increase in management efficiency, by how much would the demand for labour have to be increased?

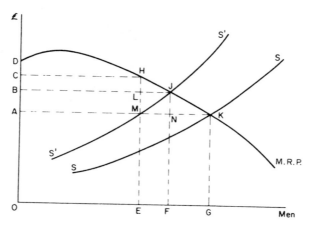

Fig. 4.4

2   A firm making sunglasses uses two factors of production: capital and labour. The amount of capital is fixed in the short run and the total product of labour per week is as follows:

Labour employed	Total pairs of sunglasses produced	Marginal physical product
1	30	
2	70	
3	115	
4	155	
5	190	
6	215	
7	230	
8	233	

   (i)   Calculate the marginal physical product of labour to complete the table.
  (ii)   At what level of employment is the average product of labour at a maximum?
 (iii)   At what level of employment is the marginal product of labour at a maximum?

The price of sunglasses is £2. Assume the firm is trying to maximize profits and is in perfect competition both in the market for sunglasses and for its labour. Plot the firm's demand curve for labour on graph paper. (Plot the marginal products between the number of workers.)

(iv) Estimate from the graph how many men the firm will employ if the wage rate is £40 per week.
(v) Estimate from the graph how many men the firm will employ if the wage rate is £60 per week.
(vi) Assume the firm is employing four workers. It now doubles its capital and its labour force. If constant returns to scale are to be expected, what would be total output?
(vii) If under the conditions of (v) above, total output were 300 pairs of sunglasses, what returns to scale are operating?
(viii) Revert to the assumption that the firm has the original amount of capital. The demand facing the firm now changes so that it must lower price from £2 to £1 if it wishes to sell 100 or more pairs of sunglasses. What wage rate would result in the firm employing six workers?

3

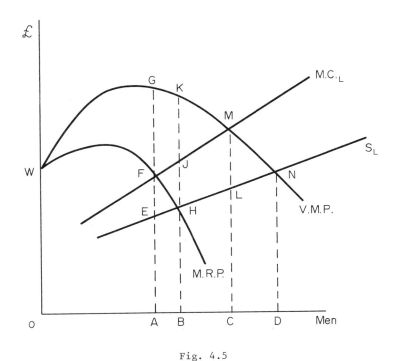

Fig. 4.5

Fig. 4.5 shows curves related to the supply and demand for labour. They are labelled as follows:

V.M.P. stands for the value of the marginal product of labour.
M.R.P. stands for the marginal revenue product of labour.
S_L stands for the supply curve of labour.
$M.C._L$ stands for the marginal cost of labour.

Assume profit maximization and answer the following.

(i) What market conditions apply to the demand for labour?
(ii) What market conditions apply to the demand for the product of labour?
(iii) What is the equilibrium wage rate?
(iv) What is the equilibrium level of employment?
(v) What is the total wage bill?
(vi) What is the total revenue available for factors of production other than labour?
(vii) If the employer was a discriminating monopolist (able to pay every worker a different wage), how many men would he employ?
(viii) In circumstances of (vii) above, what is the highest wage the employer would pay?

4 The Republic of Splosia has a population of 100 000; the birth-rate is 50 per 1000 of the population per annum, the death-rate is 20 per 1000 per annum. Ignore the effects of age distribution and, using compound interest tables, estimates to the nearest thousand

   (i)   the population size after 5 years.

  (ii)   the population size after 10 years.

 (iii)   the population size after 30 years.

  (iv)   the population size after 100 years.

   (v)   there is also a flow of immigrants and emigrants at rates of 20 per 1000 and 10 per 1000 respectively. What will the population size be after 10 years?

5 Statica has a population of 10 000 which has not changed. The national income is $1 million. The labour force is a constant proportion of the total population. An increase now occurs of 5% in the population, and a similar percentage increase in the size of the capital stock, which is the only other factor of production. Constant returns to scale are assumed. What is income per head of the population after the increase?

6

   (i)   A machine is just worth buying. It costs £1000, lasts one year, has no scrap value and yields £1100 at the end of its life. What is the marginal productivity of capital?

  (ii)   How much will £1000 be worth in 2 years' time at 6% compound interest?

 (iii)   A firm is considered buying one of two machines (I and II) each of which costs £10 000 and has no scrap value at the end of its life. I lasts 1 year and has a certain yield of £10 600 at the end. II lasts 2 years and has a certain yield of £11 100 at the end. The market rate of interest is 6%. What should the firm do?

  (iv)   The situation of (iii) above holds, except that the market rate of interest is 12%. What should the firm do?

   (v)   The situation of (iii) above holds, except that the market rate of interest is 3%. What should the firm do?

  (vi)   A business has found it just worth while to buy a machine which yields 10%. It lasts 2 years. At the end of the first year it yields £550 and at the end of the second year £1210. It has no scrap value. How much did it cost?

U.K. ECONOMY

Multiple Choice

Choose the alternative which provides the best answer to the question or completes the sentence most satisfactorily.

1 In the twenty years up to 1980 the average level of real wages in Britain

  (a)   tended to rise despite the fact that prices often rose more rapidly than wages.

  (b)   tended to fall because prices often rose more rapidly than wages.

  (c)   tended to rise because prices usually rose less rapidly than wages.

  (d)   tended to fall because prices usually rose more rapidly than wages.

  (e)   remained roughly constant because prices and wages rose at about the same rate.

2 In which of the following industries have the average weekly earnings of full-time men been (i) highest and (ii) lowest in recent years?

  (a)   Building

  (b)   Chemicals

  (c)   Clothing

  (d)   Food

  (e)   Vehicles

3 Weekly earnings of women have averaged what percentage of those of men in British industry in recent years?

  (a)   About 20%

  (b)   About 40%

  (c)   About 60%

  (d)   About 80%

  (e)   About 95%

4 The Equal Pay Act of 1976

    (a) forced employers to pay the same wage to workers regardless of their race or religion.
    (b) forced employers to pay the same wage to workers doing the same work regardless of their productivity.
    (c) forced employers to enter into negotiations with workers to introduce equal pay.
    (d) made it illegal for employers to discriminate in employment on grounds of sex.
    (e) None of the above

5 Evidence suggests that differences in (i) wage earnings and (ii) incomes between persons in Britain is due to which of the following?

    1. Age, sex and race
    2. Trade union strength
    3. Bargaining power of employers
    4. Education and training
    5. Property ownership
    6. Attitudes to work

    (a) 1 and 4 only
    (b) 2 and 3 only
    (c) 2,3,4 and 5 only
    (d) 1,2,3,4 and 6 only
    (e) 1,2,3,4,5 and 6

6 Approximately what percentage of total pre-tax personal incomes is taken by the top (i) 1% and (ii) 10% of income recipients?

    (a) 5%
    (b) 15%
    (c) 25%
    (d) 35%
    (e) 45%

7 In which of the following regions of the U.K. have (i) average earnings been highest, (ii) average earnings been lowest, (iii) unemployment rates been highest and (iv) unemployment rates been lowest in recent years?

    (a) Midlands
    (b) South East England
    (c) Scotland
    (d) Wales
    (e) Northern Ireland

8 The (i) highest and (ii) lowest percentage unemployment rate for any year between 1950 and 1980 in Britain was approximately

    (a) 0.5%.
    (b) 2%.
    (c) 4%.
    (d) 8%.
    (e) 12%.

9 The upward trend in the level of unemployment since the 1960s in Britain is probably due mainly to

    (a) the falling average age of the work force.
    (b) the decline in the amount of training for skills.
    (c) increasing regional dispersion of industry.
    (d) technological changes.
    (e) All of the above are correct.

10 The proportion of unemployment attributable to (i) frictional, (ii) structural and (iii) voluntary causes in present-day Britain is

    (a) 20%.
    (b) 40%.
    (c) 60%.
    (d) 80%.
    (e) not known at all precisely.

11 The population of the U.K. between 1881 and 1981 approximately

    (a)   doubled.
    (b)   tripled.
    (c)   quadrupled.
    (d)   quintupled.
    (e)   increased by 50%.

12 In which of the following regions of the U.K. did the population increase (i) most and (ii) least since the First World War?

    (a)   London
    (b)   Midlands
    (c)   Northern Ireland
    (d)   South East England
    (e)   Scotland

13 What proportion of the total population is the labour force in Britain?

    (a)   About 25%
    (b)   About 35%
    (c)   About 50%
    (d)   About 60%
    (e)   About 75%

14 Which of the following caused the ratio of the working to the total population to change since the Second World War?

    (a)   The tendency for people to stay on at work after reaching retirement age
    (b)   The rise in the unemployment rate
    (c)   The improvement in life expectancy
    (d)   The rise in the participation rate of married women
    (e)   The rise in the ratio of white-collar to manual workers

15 The proportion of the total population aged 65 and over is expected by the end of the present century to be approximately

    (a)   5%.
    (b)   10%.
    (c)   15%.
    (d)   20%.
    (e)   25%.

16 The proportion of (i) men and (ii) women in the work force who are members of trade unions is approximately

(a) a fifth.	(a) a fifth.
(b) a quarter.	(b) a third.
(c) a third.	(c) a half.
(d) a half.	(d) two-thirds.
(e) two-thirds.	(e) three-quarters.

17 The number of trade unions in Britain is approximately

    (a)   50.
    (b)   500.
    (c)   5000.
    (d)   50 000.
    (e)   500 000.

18 Which of the following industries have (i) the highest and (ii) the lowest percentage of their labour force enrolled as trade union members?

    (a)   Agriculture
    (b)   Building
    (c)   Mining
    (d)   Engineering
    (e)   Clothing

19 Which of the following trade unions (i) has the largest membership and (ii) comes closest to being a craft union?

(a) N.A.L.G.O.
(b) N.G.A.
(c) N.U.G.M.W.
(d) N.U.P.E.
(e) T.G.W.U.

20 Which of the following reaons accounts most probably for the growth of trade union membership since the Second World War?

(a) Rising unemployment
(b) Increasing numbers of trade unions
(c) Increasing relative importance of small establishments in manufacturing
(d) The growth of trade unionism among white-collar workers
(e) Increasing proportions of part-time workers

Exercises

Note: Sources are suggested for all exercises. Alternatives may be available if the one mentioned is not in your library. For advice on them and on the collection and presentation of data in tabular and graphical form see pp ix-x.

1 From the Annual Abstract of Statistics extract details of the numbers of births, deaths and marriages for each Census year since the beginning of the century. Next ascertain the size of the total population of the U.K. for the same years and calculate the birth-, death- and marriage-rates per thousand of the population for each year.

(i) Plot the calculated birth-, death- and marriage-rates on graph paper. Write a short paragraph describing the trends of all three rates.
(ii) Suggest reasons for the changes in any of the rates that you have observed.
(iii) How do the birth- and death-rates affect the size of the total population? What additional information must you have in order to account for the trend of the total population since the beginning of the century?
(iv) Consider carefully the likely trends in the next ten years of birth-, death- and marriage-rates. Do your conclusions suggest that the total population is likely to rise, fall or stay about the same? Compare your predictions with the official projections of the government actuary (in the Annual Abstract of Statistics). Can you offer any ideas on why they might differ?

2 Collect figures for the numbers of the population of Great Britain aged 15 and over in the categories shown in the following table for the most recent year available.

	Males		Females	
	Numbers (000s)	%	Numbers (000s)	%
	(i)	(ii)	(iii)	(iv)
1. In employment				
2. Unemployed				
3. Total economically active				
4. Students				
5. Retired				
6. Total population aged 15 and over		100%		100%

Source: Annual Abstract of Statistics

(i) Calculate the percentages in each category in Cols (ii) and (iv).
(ii) How much higher are the activity rates for men than for women? Can you suggest explanations for the difference?
(iii) Find out whether the particular year to which the statistics in the table refer was one when the total national output was higher or lower than average. How do you think that the percentages in rows 1 and 2 would be affected by this?
(iv) What are the main determinants of the percentages in rows 4 and 5 of the table?

3 For each major industry group find the numbers registered as unemployed and the estimated numbers of employees and express the former as percentages of the latter. In which industries are unemployment rates relatively high and low? Can you suggest why? (Take what are known as the main 'Orders' of the Standard Industrial Classification as your industry headings — see Appendix to the Annual Abstract of Statistics.)

4 The Monthly Digest of Statistics (or the Employment Gazette) contains details of the numbers unemployed (U) and the numbers of notified job vacancies (V) by region of the U.K. Enter these figures for a recent date in columns (i) and (ii) of the following table and calculate U as a percentage of V for each region in order to complete column (iii) Finally add percentage rates of unemployment in column (iv). Rank separately the statistics in the last two columns.

Region	Unemployed (Nos.) (U) (i)	Vacancies (V) (ii)	$\frac{(i)}{(ii)}$ x 100 (iii)	Unemployment Rate (%) (iv)	Rank col. (iii) (v)	Order col. (iv) (vi)
South East						
East Anglia						
South West						
West Midlands						
East Midlands						
Yorks + Humber						
North West						
Northern						
Wales						
Scotland						
N. Ireland						
All regions						

Source: ....

  (i) Which regions come out at or near the top and bottom of the 'league tables'? Can you suggest why?
  (ii) What factors might explain why a region might be high in the U-V ranking (col. (v)) and relatively low in the unemployment rate ranking (col. (vi))?
  (iii) What economic forces might cause regional differences in unemployment rates to diminish. Why do they not bring about complete equality?

5 Obtain details from the Annual Abstract of Statistics of hours worked and earnings of manual workers over the last 5 years as follows:

       average weekly earnings
       average hours worked
       basic wage rates
       average hourly earnings (including and excluding overtime and bonuses)

Write a short paragraph describing the movements in each of the above. Which of them are dependent on which others? In which years have the average weekly earnings changed most rapidly? Can you suggest why?

6 Prepare a graph (known as a scatter diagram) showing the relationship between unemployment rates (per cent) and the percentage change in average weekly earnings of manual workers for the last 5 years.

The annual percentage changes in earnings may be calculated from the data collected for exercise 4 above, or from the Annual Abstract of Statistics, which is the source for unemployment rates. Use the horizontal axis for unemployment and the vertical axis for earnings. Plot one point for each year showing the association between the two statistics. Label each point with the year to which it relates.

  (i) Is there any clear association between the two variables shown in the scatter diagram? If so, why? If not, why not?
  (ii) If the two variables appear to be correlated, does this imply that one is the cause of the other? If so, which do you think is the dependent and which is the independent variable?
  (iii) Prepare a second scatter diagram similar to the first but substituting changes in real earnings (i.e. money earnings deflated by a price index) for the changes in nominal earnings. Is any apparent correlation better or worse? Explain in words the meaning of the two diagrams and any differences between them.

7 Obtain figures from the Employment Gazette (published monthly by the Department of Employment and available in most public libraries) of the average hourly earnings of all manual workers in the industries listed in the following table and complete column (i). Add figures of the rise or fall (%) in earnings over the last 5 years (from the Annual Abstract of Statistics).

Industry	Average earnings	
	19.... (i)	Percentage change 19.... to 19.... (ii)
Food, drink, tobacco		
Chemicals		
Metal manufacture		
Engineering, mech.		
Engineering, elec.		
Shipbuilding		
Vehicles		
Textiles		
Clothing		
Construction		
Transport		

Source: ....

(i)   Which industries had the highest (i) average earnings in the latest year and (ii) the greatest increase in the last 5 years? Which had the lowest increase in the last 5 years?

(ii) Consider carefully whether (a) supply and/or (b) demand can explain your answers to (i) above.

(iii) What market forces do you think might act to change the pattern of inter-industry differentials you identified in (i) above in the immediate future?

8 From the Annual Abstract of Statistics find out the average weekly earnings of manual workers, male and female, in the most recent year available and another 10 years previously. Can you explain the sex differential in terms of supply and demand? Has the differential changed over the period. Can you suggest why or why not?

9 Complete the following table showing the numbers of trade unions and the numbers of their members, for unions of the different size listed. Express the numbers as percentages of the totals in columns (ii) and (iv).

Size of union (numbers of members)	Numbers of unions		Numbers of members	
	Nos. (i)	% (ii)	Nos. (iii)	% (iv)
Under 500				
500 - 2499				
2500 - 24 999				
25 000 - 99 999				
100 000 - 249 999				
250 000 and over				
All		100%		100%

Source: Annual Abstract of Statistics

(i)   Do the figures in the table suggest that there are a large number of small unions or a small number of large ones or both?

(ii) How does the size distribution of trade unions differ from that of, say, 20 years ago. What are the main reasons for the changes?

(iii) From either Whitaker's Almanac or The Times 1000 find the names of six trade unions with over a quarter of a million members. Which are craft, industrial and general workers' unions?

(iv) How far do you think it is true that the large unions you discovered in (iii) above have the strongest bargaining power?

10 Find out the approximate price of land in your area of each of the following kinds, and reduce them to a comparable basis (e.g. £ per sq. metre).

> Private residential land near a council estate
> Private residential land in a high income area
> Land for office building in the town centre
> Land for shop premises in the town centre
> The nearest agricultural land

(i) Which is the highest price and lowest price land? What part, if any, does economic rent play in explaining the price differences?

(ii) What economic forces, if any, might act in such a way as to reduce such differentials. What stops them from bringing about complete equality in the price of land for all uses?

11 Prepare a graph showing the share of each of the following in total national income over the last 10 years (Source: Annual Abstract of Statistics)

> Income from employment
> Income from self-employment
> Gross trading profits of companies
> Rent

(i) Which are the largest and the smallest components on the above list?

(ii) Which of the components has increased or decreased most over the period? Can changes in supply and/or demand help explain why?

(iii) Does the marginal productivity theory of factor prices help explain the differing factor shares you have found? How or why not?

12 The Annual Abstract of Statistics contains a table which gives details of the total numbers of incomes and the total income received by different income size classes before tax. Calculate the percentages of the total numbers of income and of total income for each category. Cumulate the percentages (e.g. the share of the lowest 20% of income includes the share of the lowest 10%. Plot the cumulate percentages on the graph below to yield a Lorenz curve.

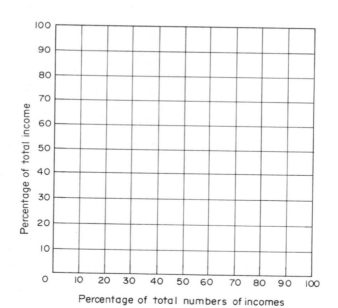

Fig. 4.6

(i) Read from the graph the share of total income received by the top 1%, 10%, 20% and 50% of the total number of income units. Can you tell from the graph how equally or unequally incomes are distributed in Britain?

(ii) Why does the graph tell you very little about the size distribution of the earnings of labour as a factor of production?

(iii) What are the principal reans why, as the graph shows, some people have higher incomes than others?

Essays

1. 'There is no essential difference in the way in which price is determined in the markets for factors of production from that in the markets for goods and services.' Discuss.

2. What do you understand by the law of diminishing returns? Is it possible for a firm to be operating at a point where expansion of output could bring either diminishing returns or economies of large-scale production?

3. How far does the marginal productivity theory of distribution imply that intervention to regulate wages is pointless?

4. Explain the difference between the law of diminishing returns and the law of returns to scale.

5. What do you understand by the statement that the elasticity of demand for labour by a particular firm is high? To what could it be attributed?

6. What is implied by a backward-sloping supply curve of labour?

7. Do you expect agriculture to be more subject to the law of diminishing returns than manufacturing industry?

8. In what ways do the income and substitution effects of a change in wage rates on the supply of labour differ from those of a change in the price of a commodity on the demand for it?

9. Explain why an increase in wage rates may sometimes increase and sometimes decrease the supply of labour.

10. A firm switches from one system of wage payment to a new and popular one, raising both productivity and the number of men seeking employment. Use economic analysis to show how the level of wages in the firm might rise, fall or remain unchanged.

11. How far is there a tendency for incomes to become equal in a market economy such as that of the U.K.?

12. Consider the effect on the level of wage rates of the introduction of a law limiting weekly hours of work to a maximum of 35.

13. How might you explain a tendency for differentials between skilled and unskilled workers to decline over a long period of time?

14. How can you explain the fact that the average earnings of women in Britain are substantially below those of men?

15. Why do accountants usually earn more than shop assistants?

16. Comment on the observation that the best jobs seem to get the best pay.

17. How important to a trade union in its wage negotiations is the existence of a closed shop?

18. What circumstances would help a trade union to raise the wages of its members without causing unemployment?

19. What information is needed in order to be able to predict the size of the future population for a country? How much of it is available for the U.K.?

20. What are the economic arguments for limiting the number of immigrants into Britain? Are there any economic counter-arguments?

21. What measures would you suggest to stimulate an increase in the size of Britain's working population?

22. Why are shop rents in central London greater than in country towns?

23. Is there any relationship at all between the meaning of rent in everyday use and that employed by economists when using the term 'economic rent'?

24. Explain why economic rent is the producer's counterpart of consumer's surplus.

25. Is the cost of capital better regarded as its value in alternative uses or as the rate of interest that has to be paid for borrowing?

26. How does the rate of interest enter into calculations of the profitability of investment projects?

27. What is meant by the present value of a stream of future incomes? How is such a concept related to the marginal efficiency of capital?

28. In what sense can interest be considered as the price of time?

29. What is the purpose of discounting the yield of different investment projects?

30. Is the rate of interest a reward for refraining from consumption, the cost of borrowing in order to finance investment in capital, the reward for undertaking investment or all three?

31. What are the implications of a rate of interest equal to 1%, 0% and -1%?

32. What is meant by the statement that profits are the reward to entrepreneurship?

33. To what extent is it true to say that all shareholders and debenture holders control a company like I.C.I. Ltd.?

34. Compare and contrast the different meanings given to the word profit in economics.

35. A 'spec' builder has used £20 000 of his savings to construct a new house. Would you regard the financial return he derives as being of the nature of rent, interest or profit?

CHAPTER 5

National Income

Economic theory is conventionally divided into two main areas: (1) problems of resource allocation and price determination in individual markets, and (2) the determination of the level of national income. The first of these areas is the subject of microeconomics. The second is that of MACROECONOMICS. Here the economist stands back, as it were, to look through the 'wrong end' of a telescope to observe the working of the whole economy.

There are many relationships and interactions to be studied from the macroeconomic viewpoint. What they have in common is that the concern is with AGGREGATES (or totals). Thus, in contrast to microeconomics, where we talk, for example, of the consumption of (demand for) apricots, butter, cars, etc., in macroeconomics we talk of aggregate consumption expenditure on all consumer goods and services. Similarly, output in macroeconomics is the national output and the level of prices is the (average) general level of prices, ignoring changes in the relative prices of individual goods.

This chapter opens with a number of questions on the nature of the NATIONAL INCOME, its identity with NATIONAL PRODUCT and NATIONAL EXPENDITURE, and with the different methods by which it may be measured. You should make sure that you understand the meaning of VALUE ADDED, the difference between income and wealth (a FLOW and a STOCK), between GROSS values and NET (the difference being DEPRECIATION or CAPITAL CONSUMPTION), between values at FACTOR COST and at MARKET PRICES (the differences being net taxes on expenditure), between NATIONAL and DOMESTIC product (the difference being net property income from abroad) and between factor payments and TRANSFERS (the distinction resting on whether payments are made in return for factor services or not in order to avoid DOUBLE COUNTING). The national income is measured in money terms. Though related to, it is not the same as the STANDARD OF LIVING and the two may diverge if, among other things, there is a change in the total population, in the prices or quality of goods and services, or in the distribution of income, either between persons or between consumption and other components of output.

The determination of the national income and other macroeconomic aggregates, especially the general levels of prices and employment, is a controversial area in economics. The two main schools of thought are known as KEYNESIAN and MONETARIST and the differences between them are discussed in the final chapter (see p.129). The approach here emphasizes the determination of real income (basically Keynesian), while monetary influences are dealt with in the next chapter.

The starting-point of the theory makes use of the notion of AGGREGATE DEMAND. It is easy to show its importance. Incomes are received as a direct and immediate consequence of someone's expenditure. The butcher earns an income because people spend money buying his goods, so does the baker, the candlestick-maker, and so on. Our concern is, therefore, with aggregate expenditure and its determinants in order to arrive at an understanding of the conditions under which the national income can be said to be at an equilibrium level.

The simplest model used to outline the theory of income (Y) determination assumes a closed economy without government. The two components of aggregate demand are CONSUMPTION (C) and INVESTMENT (I).

Consumption refers to expenditure by persons (or households) on goods and services which satisfy immediate needs. The total amount of consumption in a period is influenced by a number of social, psychological and institutional factors, such as the availability of credit, the assortment of goods available and innate thriftiness. In the short run these are assumed to remain unchanged and the prime determinant of consumption emphasized is the level of income. The relationship between C and Y is called the PROPENSITY TO CONSUME. It can take the form of a table or schedule of varying consumption expenditures at different levels of income. Alternatively, it may be plotted on a graph, in which case it normally appears as an upward-sloping curve, since the relationship between C and Y tends to be positive, i.e. a change in income leads to a change in the same direction in consumption. (This is what is meant when it is said that consumption is an increasing function of income.) A change in a consumption determinant other than income implies a shift of the entire consumption curve (or CONSUMPTION FUNCTION.) The proportion of income consumed at any income level (C/Y) is known as the AVERAGE PROPENSITY TO CONSUME, while the relationship between a change in income and the corresponding change in consumption ($\Delta C/\Delta Y$) is called the MARGINAL PROPENSITY TO CONSUME.

Investment contrasts with consumption and is, in fact, best defined as spending on goods and services other than for current consumption. The principal component of investment consists of capital goods, like machines and factories, which are wanted, not for themselves, but because they indirectly help to produce more consumer goods in the future. Investment expenditure is of two kinds: (1) fixed investment in the acquisition of capital goods and (2) changes in STOCKS (inventories in American texts) of goods and materials in the hands of businesses. An increase or decrease in such stocks constitutes positive or negative investment respectively.

A first approach to the theory of income determination often assumes that investment expenditure is constant and unrelated to the level of income. The determinants of investment are complex, and its future level far more difficult to predict accurately than is that of consumption. There are two main theories of investment. One is a development from microeconomics and considers the matter from the viewpoint of a business firm, comparing the expected yield on investment (the marginal efficiency of capital) with its cost (the rate of interest) and the availability of finance (see p.54). The second theory makes investment depend on income. The nature of the dependence may be direct and related to the level of income, when a PROPENSITY TO INVEST is incorporated into the analysis. Alternatively, investment may be determined by the rate at which income changes over time. Such a theory of invest-ment is called the ACCELERATOR (or the ACCELERATION PRINCIPLE) and it provides an explanation of the observed fact that investment expenditures fluctuate much more widely than do those of consumption.

Equilibrium income (in a model without government or foreign trade) occurs at the level at which total desired expenditure on consumption plus investment is exactly equal to the level of income itself. Only in this case is income just, and only just, sufficient to purchase total output. If planned expenditure exceeds (or falls short of) national output, unplanned stocks of goods and materials will fall (or rise) and income itself will tend to rise (or fall). Fluctuations in income and output tend to follow a cyclical pattern, known as the TRADE (or BUSINESS) CYCLE, and unemployment in periods of depression due to a deficiency of aggregate demand is called CYCLICAL (or DEMAND DEFICIENT) UNEMPLOYMENT.

An alternative view of the same process makes use of the notions of INJECTIONS into and WITHDRAWALS from the flow of income and expenditure, consisting respectively of income spent and not spent, other than on household consumption. Investment is such an injection. Saving is a withdrawal (or LEAKAGE).

The schedules (curves) of savings and investment represent planned levels at different incomes. These desired levels will also be those actually achieved in equilibrium, but not otherwise. If the plans of the community for saving and investing exactly coincide, then total investment expenditure is precisely the same as the portion of its income that the community does not plan to consume (i.e. plans to save). Total planned expenditure is, therefore, equal to income which is an equilibrium. If, on the other hand, savings and investment plans do not coincide, income is not at an equilibrium level, and both cannot be realized. For example, suppose that planned savings exceed planned investment. Businesses may find an unplanned increase in their stocks of unsold goods, which will lead them to cut back production so that income falls. It should be noted that, while planned saving and investment (withdrawals and injections) are equal only in equilibrium, actual savings and investment are always identical. This follows from the accounting definitions that income which is not consumed is saved, and expenditure which is not on consumption is investment. Synonyms used for planned and actual savings (and investment) are as follows: intended, desired and ex ante for planned; realized, achieved and ex post for actual. (A parallel may be drawn here with supply and demand in microeconomics. The supply and demand curves are planned or desired relationships. If the quantities demanded and supplied are not the same because price is not at an equilibrium, then price tends to change. In equilibrium, the quantity desired to be purchased is equal to the quantity desired to be sold. But even at a price which is not an equilibrium price, the actual quantity bought must always equal the actual quantity sold. They are equal by (accounting) definition.)

The questions and problems in this chapter make use of two kinds of diagrams — the so-called 45-degree type, which measure income (on the horizontal axis) against expenditure (on the vertical axis), and those with the corresponding savings and investment curves. Reference is made also to the MULTIPLIER, defined as the number of times by which a change in autonomous expenditure must be multiplied in order to arrive at the consequent change in income. The multiplier can only bring about a change in real, as distinct from money, income if there are unused resources available. An increase in expenditure at full employment, on the other hand, leads only to a rise in the money value of the national income through an inflation of the general price level. An excess of aggregate expenditure over income in these circumstances is sometimes called an inflationary gap. However the theory of inflation requires consideration of AGGREGATE SUPPLY (the quantities of goods and services that businesses wish to produce) and this subject is taken up in the next chapter.

The theory of income determination outlined above can be extended to an open economy, with foreign transactions, with a government sector, with taxes and with public expenditures. The international implications of the theory are further dealt with in Chapter 7. It is sufficient here to point out that imports (M) are positively associated with income (there is a MARGINAL PROPENSITY TO IMPORT), but are, like savings, leakages. Exports (X), in contrast, create incomes and are therefore injections, like investment. Similarly, in the case of an economy with a government sector, taxes (T) and government expenditures (G) are leakages and injections respectively. The equilibrium condition for an open economy with a government sector is that total planned expenditures of all kinds must equal output or that planned: S + M + T = I + X + G.

ANALYSIS

Multiple Choice

Choose the alternative which provides the best answer to the question or completes the sentence most satisfactorily.

IMPORTANT NOTE: Many of the answers to questions on the theory of income determination depend crucially on the assumptions made, e.g. whether the economy has a government sector (with taxes and government expenditure) and whether it is an open or closed economy (with or without foreign transactions). The questions in this chapter are based on a simple 'Keynesian model'. Unless otherwise stated, consumption is assumed to be a function of income, and investment is autonomous (i.e. not a function of income).

UNLESS EXPLICITLY STATED TO THE CONTRARY YOU SHOULD ASSUME THAT A QUESTION REFERS TO A CLOSED ECONOMY WITHOUT A GOVERNMENT SECTOR.

1 In a closed economy without a government sector the national income is the same as

(a) national expenditure on goods and services.
(b) national product.
(c) national output of consumption and investment goods.
(d) total value added in the economy.
(e) All of the above.

2 The following stages occur in the production and distribution of a scarf. The farmer sells wool to a spinner for 60p. The spinner sells the yarn to a weaver for £1.00. The weaver sells the cloth to a wholesaler for £1.20. The wholesaler sells the scarf for £2.00 to a retailer who sells it to the final consumer for £2.50. What is the value added by the wholesaler?

(a) 50p
(b) 80p
(c) £1.20
(d) £3.30
(e) £4.50

3 Which of the following is a current flow item as distinct from a stock?

(a) The national wealth
(b) The change in the stock of raw materials during the year
(c) The balance sheet assets of companies
(d) The total road vehicles in the country on 1 January
(e) The investment in capital equipment inherited from last year

4 Which of the following would cause an immediate rise in (i) the real national income and (ii) the standard of living of the population of a country?

1. A rise in investment expenditure
2. A rise in consumption expenditure
3. A rise in the general price level
4. A fall in the birth-rate
5. A fall in costs of production
6. An improvement in the quality of goods

(a) 1,2 and 5 only
(b) 3,5 and 6 only
(c) 1,3 and 4 only
(d) 2,4,5 and 6 only
(e) 1,2,3,4,5 and 6

5 The difference between Gross Domestic Product and Gross National Product is equal to

(a) the value of exports minus the value of imports.
(b) net property income from aborad.
(c) net foreign lending.
(d) the value of overseas assets.
(e) the income of non-residents.

6 Gross national product at factor cost <u>plus</u> taxes <u>less</u> subsidies on expenditure is equal to

(a)   gross national income at market prices.
(b)   net national product at factor cost.
(c)   net national income at factor cost.
(d)   gross national product net of transfer payments.
(e)   personal disposable income net of depreciation.

7 When calculating a country's net national income, transfer payments such as the following should be excluded:

(a)   depreciation.
(b)   widowers' payments to their housekeepers.
(c)   profits of companies not paid out as dividends.
(d)   imputed rents of owner-occupied houses.
(e)   None of the above.

8 Which of the following additions to and deductions from national income at market prices are made to give disposible income?

Deductions	Additions
1. Taxes on income	4. Transfer payments
2. Taxes on expenditure	5. Dividend payments to persons
3. Government borrowing	

(a)   1 only
(b)   4 and 5 only
(c)   1 and 4 only
(d)   2,3 and 5 only
(e)   1,2,3,4 and 5

9 The following information relates to a country which does not engage in any foreign transactions. What is the value of its GNP at factor cost?

Consumers expenditure	2000
Net capital formation	250
Capital consumption	50
Taxes on income	600
Taxes on expenditure	500
Subsidies	100

(a)   1200
(b)   1800
(c)   1900
(d)   2700
(e)   2900

10 A knowledge of the propensity to consume schedule is sufficient information to be able to derive

(a)   the propensity to save schedule.
(b)   the level of income.
(c)   the equilibrium level of income.
(d)   the level of investment.
(e)   None of the above.

11 One reason why total consumption sometimes exceeds total income is that

(a)   people can save more than their income.
(b)   in times of relative depression firms lower prices to get rid of stocks of unsold goods.
(c)   people can obtain goods on credit.
(d)   in times of boom people lose their incentive to save.
(e)   the rich make charitable gifts of goods for other people to consume.

12 The main determinant of changes in aggregate saving in the short run is changes in

(a)   income.
(b)   thrift.
(c)   the rate of interest.
(d)   family circumstances.
(e)   the size of the population.

13 If the marginal propensity to save of the rich is greater than that of the poor, then a redistribution of income from poor to rich will raise

(a) consumption out of a given income.
(b) saving out of a given income.
(c) both consumption and saving out of a given income.
(d) neither consumption nor saving out of a given income.
(e) the average propensity to consume.

14 The table below gives details of the total consumption expenditure at different income levels for an economy.

Income	Consumption
0	300
1000	1200
2000	2000
3000	2700
4000	3200
5000	3000

Which of the following statements is correct?

(a) The average propensity to save at income 5000 is 1.25.
(b) The average propensity to consume at income 4000 is 0.7.
(c) The marginal propensity to save between incomes of 3000 and 4000 is 0.5.
(d) The marginal propensity to save between incomes of 2000 and 3000 is 0.7.
(e) The marginal propensity to consume between incomes of 1000 and 2000 is 1.25.

15 Which of the following is <u>least</u> likely to affect personal consumption expenditure out of a given income?

(a) A change in the stock of assets held by households
(b) A change in price expectations of consumers
(c) A redistribution of income from high to low income groups
(d) A change in the level of business confidence
(e) The appearance of a new range of consumer durables

16 The accelerator will cause larger year-to-year fluctuations in investment

(a) the smaller the proportion of capital that needs replacement each year.
(b) the more excess capacity exists in the economy.
(c) the less business men believe that the increase is permanent.
(d) the more difficult it is to obtain finance.
(e) the more investment is autonomous rather than induced.

17 The multiplier is the factor by which

(a) an increase in expenditure raises investment.
(b) an increase in investment lowers income.
(c) a change in income changes investment.
(d) a change in income changes saving.
(e) a change in autonomous expenditure changes income.

18 Which of the following is <u>least</u> likely to affect private investment expenditure?

(a) The availability of credit
(b) The level of income
(c) The rate of interest
(d) The taxation of personal wealth
(e) The state of business confidence

19 If the aggregate consumption curve coincides with the 45° line then the aggregate saving curve

(a) must be parallel to the 45° line.
(b) bisects the angle made by the 45° line and the horizontal axis.
(c) has no determinate position.
(d) lies along the horizontal axis.
(e) also lies along the 45° line.

20 All the following items of expenditure, with one exception, are classed as investment. Which is the exception?

(a) Factory construction
(b) A computer
(c) Stocks of coal by business
(d) Stocks or shares in a joint-stock company
(e) Increases in stocks of unsold goods

21 Which of the following terms covers persons (i) who are in long-term unemployment following a change in the pattern of demand and (ii) who do not bother to look for work because the economic climate is depressed?

(a) Cyclical unemployment
(b) Frictional unemployment
(c) Hidden unemployment
(d) Seasonal unemployment
(e) Structural unemployment

22 According to the theory of the accelerator

(a) investment changes by a multiple of any change in income.
(b) investment changes by a multiple of any change in the rate of interest.
(c) investment changes by a multiple of any change in the marginal efficiency of capital.
(d) income changes by a multiple of any change in investment.
(e) income changes by a multiple of any change in investment plus saving.

23 If the community plans to save more than it plans to invest

(a) the community must save less than it intended.
(b) the community must invest more than it intended.
(c) the community will actually save and invest the same amount.
(d) the general level of prices will tend to rise.
(e) income will tend to rise.

24 In an open economy with a government sector, which of the following are (i) withdrawals from and (ii) injections into the circular flow of income and expenditure?

1. Savings
2. Investment expenditure
3. Stocks of goods and services
4. Accumulated past savings
5. Government expenditure
6. Imports
7. Exports
8. Consumption expenditure

(a) 1 and 2 only
(b) 1 and 6 only
(c) 2,5 and 7 only
(d) 1,3,4 and 6 only
(e) 2,4,5,7 and 8 only

25 Which of the following is a definition of the term (i) aggregate demand and (ii) aggregate supply as used by economists?

(a) The total value of output achieved in an economy
(b) The quantity of goods and services that businesses wish to produce
(c) The total consumption and investment expenditure that the community wish to undertake
(d) The total savings and investment expenditure that is made
(e) The relationship between the value of output and the general price level

26 Equilibrium income is that level at which

(a) there is full employment.
(b) the community is spending exactly all of its income on consumption.
(c) actual saving is equal to actual investment.
(d) the amount which society wishes to spend on investment is equal to the amount which it wishes to spend on consumption.
(e) the amount which society wishes to spend on investment is equal to the amount of its income which it does not wish to spend on consumption.

27 If planned savings exceed planned investment the result will be

   (a) an unplanned rise in stocks.
   (b) a rise in the national income.
   (c) a rise in the general level of prices.
   (d) a fall in planned investment.
   (e) a rise in planned savings.

28

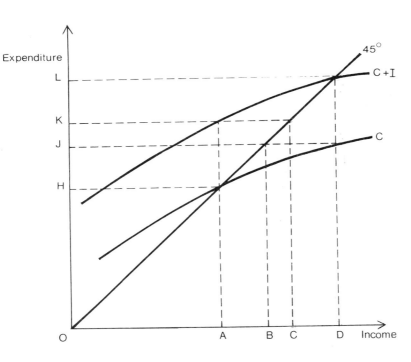

Fig. 5.1

Fig. 5.1 shows the consumption functions in a closed economy without a government sector. What is (i) equilibrium income and (ii) what is the average propensity to save at equilibrium?

	(i)		(ii)
(a)	OA	(a)	JL/CD
(b)	OB	(b)	OL/OD
(c)	OC	(c)	JL/OL
(d)	OD	(d)	OJ/OD
(e)	Anywhere on the 45° line	(e)	HK/OA

29 The table below shows the amounts that an economy plans to spend out of its income at different income levels. Planned investment expenditure is 200. What is the equilibrium level of income?

Income	Consumption expenditure
1000	1600
2000	2400
3000	3200
4000	4000
5000	4800

   (a) 1000
   (b) 2000
   (c) 3000
   (d) 4000
   (e) 5000

30 A closed economy without a government sector always spends 80% of its income on consumption and invests 500. What are (i) equilibrium income and (ii) the value of the multiplier?

<u>(i) Income</u>   (ii) Multiplier

(a) 400   (a) 2
(b) 2500   (b) 4
(c) 4000   (c) 5
(d) 5000   (d) 8
(e) It cannot be calculated   (e) It cannot be calculated
     without more information.   without more information.

31 In a closed economy without a government sector, total planned expenditure on consumption is equal to three-quarters of income and investment is zero. Equilibrium income is

(a) where investment is one-quarter of income.
(b) where savings are one-quarter of income.
(c) where the marginal propensity to save is equal to 0.75.
(d) zero.
(e) 250.

32 The effect of a fall in investment on income is normally

(a) equal to the fall in investment itself.
(b) equal to the fall in investment unless savings increase at the same time.
(c) greater than the fall in investment.
(d) greater than the fall in investment <u>because</u> savings must increase.
(e) less than the fall in investment.

33 Which of the following is the most likely reason why total income tends to fluctuate?

(a) Consumption is not always a constant fraction of income.
(b) People adjust to changing incomes by changing saving habits.
(c) Consumption habits often undergo dramatic changes.
(d) Many savings and investment decisions are taken by different people.
(e) Changes in income do not appear to have much influence on investment.

34 Which of the following is most likely to fluctuate in the short run?

(a) Employment incomes
(b) Consumption expenditure
(c) Fixed capital formation
(d) Stocks of goods
(e) Expenditure on dwellings

35 An economy is at the equilibrium level of income. If the marginal propensity to consume rises while the average propensity to consume remains unchanged this implies a

(a) movement downwards along the aggregate consumption curve.
(b) movement upwards along the aggregate saving curve.
(c) downward shift of the entire saving curve.
(d) downward shift of the entire consumption curve.
(e) change in the slope of the aggregate saving curve.

36

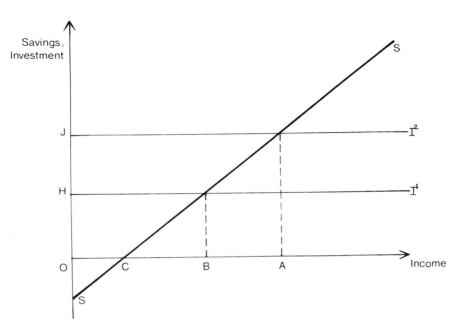

Fig. 5.2

Fig. 5.2 shows the savings and two investment functions of a closed economy without a government sector. Which of the following conclusions can be drawn from the diagram?

(a) The value of the multiplier is BA/HJ.
(b) The value of the average propensity to save is HJ/OA.
(c) The value of the marginal propensity to save is BA/HJ.
(d) The value of the marginal propensity to consume is HJ/BA.
(e) The marginal propensity to save is negative at income levels below OC.

37 Which of the following is the condition for income to be in equilibrium for a closed economy (i) without and (ii) with a government sector? (Note S stands for planned savings, I stands for planned investment, G stands for government expenditure and T stands for government revenue from taxation.)

(a) I = S
(b) G = T
(c) S + G = I + T
(d) S - I = T - G
(e) I + G - S = T

38 Suppose that the marginal propensity to consume is currently four-fifths. Which of the following policies will cause the biggest <u>fall</u> in the value of the multiplier?

(a) Raising family allowances by 25% with no corresponding increase in taxation
(b) Raising the marginal propensity to save to one-third
(c) Lowering the marginal propensity to save to one-sixth
(d) Introducing a marginal propensity to invest of 10%
(e) Lowering the marginal propensity to consume to three-quarters

39 A closed economy is in equilibrium at the point where plans to save and to invest are equal. Government expenditure must then be

(a) zero.
(b) larger than government income.
(c) negative.
(d) equal to government income.
(e) smaller than government income.

40 At full employment income, which of the following would be most likely to lead to inflation in
a closed economy?

   (a) A fall in taxation with unchanged government expenditure
   (b) A rise in the propensity to save with unchanged investment
   (c) A fall in investment with an unchanged propensity to consume
   (d) A redistribution of income from low to high income groups
   (e) An increase in productivity without any increase in wages

41 In an open economy without a government sector the immediate effect of an increase in the value
of exports will be to lead to a

   (a) fall in planned investment.
   (b) fall in imports.
   (c) rise in consumption expenditure.
   (d) rise in planned saving.
   (e) rise in national income.

Problems

1 Calculate the value of the multiplier in the following circumstances:

   (i)   The marginal propensity to consume is 0.95.
   (ii)   The marginal propensity to save is 0.2.
   (iii) The average propensity to consume is constant and equal to five-sixths of income.
   (iv)   The marginal propensity to save is 0.5. Allow time to elapse for two 'rounds' of
          expenditure only.
   (v)   The marginal propensity to consume out of disposable income is 0.8, and there is a 25%
          income tax.

2

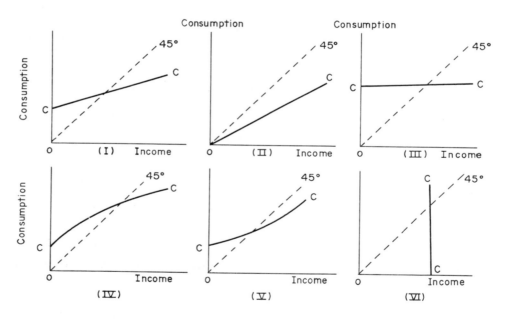

Fig. 5.3

Six aggregate consumption curves are shown in Fig. 5.3. Each is labelled c.

In which diagram or diagrams

   (i)   is consumption a fixed amount?
   (ii)   does consumption rise as income rises?
   (iii)   does consumption fall as income rises?
   (iv)   is consumption negative at low incomes?
   (v)   is consumption greater than income at low incomes?
   (vi)   is consumption less than income at all incomes?
   (vii)   is consumption greater than income at all incomes?
   (viii) is the marginal propensity to consume constant?
   (ix)   is the average propensity to consume constant?
   (x)   are both the marginal and the average propensity to consume constant?
   (xi)   does the marginal propensity to consume rise as income rises?
   (xii)   does the marginal propensity to consume fall as income rises?
   (xiii) does the average propensity to consume rise as income rises?
   (xiv)   does the average propensity to consume rise as income falls?

3

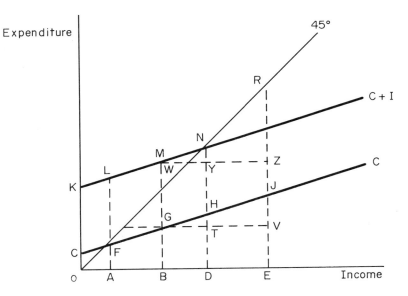

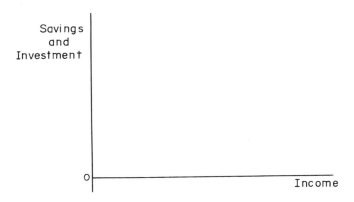

Fig. 5.4

Examine Fig. 5.4. What is

  (i)   equilibrium income?
 (ii)   the average propensity to consume at income OE?
(iii)   the marginal propensity to consume between incomes OB and OD?
 (iv)   investment at income OA?
  (v)   saving at income OE?
 (vi)   full employment income?
(vii)   In the lower part of the diagram draw the savings and investment curves deriving from the upper part of the diagram.

4 The relationship between savings (S) and income (Y) is described by the equation $S = -50 + \frac{1}{5} Y$. Fill in the second and third columns in the table below. Express the economic relationship of the equation in words.

Income (i)	Savings (ii)	Consumption (iii)
0		
100		
200		
300		
400		
500		

5 In the economy of Mythica the following relationships hold:

(a) Investment does not vary with income but is a constant 40.
(b) Consumption consists of two elements, one autonomous and the other related to disposable income. The autonomous element is 120, and in addition consumption always rises by four-fifths of any change in income.

Plot the aggregate demand curve on graph paper.

(i) What is the value of total demand if income is zero?
(ii) What is the value of total demand if income is 500?
(iii) What is the average propensity to consume when income is 500?
(iv) What is the marginal propensity to consume when income is 500?
(v) What is the equilibrium level of income?
(vi) What is the value of the multiplier?
(vii) The original conditions of the question apply except that investment falls spontaneously to 20.

   (a) What is the new equilibrium level of income?
   (b) What is the average propensity to save at equilibrium?

(viii) The original conditions of the question apply except that the government now levies a 25% income tax, none of which is spent. What is the new equilibrium level of income?
(ix) The original conditions of the question apply. What change in the level of investment would make the equilibrium level of income 1000?

6 A tape-recorder manufacturer needs one machine costing £100 for every 50 units he makes. Last year, as in previous years, he sold 1000 recorders and he has 20 machines. The life of a machine is 20 years and he replaces one each year. (In all cases ignore fractions of a machine.)

(i) What was the money value of his total investment demand last year?

Demand for tape-recorders rises by 20% to 1200 this year, and he decides to increase capital to meet it.

(ii) What is the value of new investment demand this year?
(iii) What is the value of replacement demand this year?
(iv) What is the value of total investment demand this year?
(v) What is the percentage change in total investment demand this year compared with last year?

Demand for (and sales of) tape-recorders rises again next year by a further 200.

(vi) What will the total investment demand be next year?
(vii) What will be the percentage change in investment demand next year compared with this year?
(viii) All information is unchanged except that machine life is only 2 years so that half are replaced annually. What is the percentage change in total investment demand this year compared with last year?

7 The economy of Whimsica has no government nor dealings with foreigners. From the following details for the year 2000 calculate (i) its gross national product, (ii) its gross national income and (iii) its gross national expenditure.

	£m
Value added by manufacturing industry	5500
Gross investment	2000
Wages and salaries	6000
Consumption expenditure	6500
Gross company income	1500
Value added by non-manufacturing industries	3000
Rent and self-employed income	1000

8 The national accounts of the economy of Pyromania (which does not engage in any international transactions) for a past year have been partly destroyed by fire and only the following details have been saved. It is known only that sufficient remains for the national product to be calculated in one of the conventional ways. Calculate (i) the gross national product at market prices, (ii) the net national product at market prices, (iii) the net national product at factor cost, and (iv) the gross domestic product (at factor cost).

	£m
Gross fixed investment	1000
Retained profits of companies	600
Value of stocks at 1 January	250
Rent, dividends and interest	800
Government expenditure on goods and services	300
Value of non-manufacturing output	1800
Retirement pensions	900
Net fixed investment	700
Net property income from abroad	650
Private consumption expenditure	2000
Income of the self-employed	100
Taxes on expenditure	500
Value of stocks at 31 December	450

U.K. ECONOMY

Multiple Choice

Choose the alternative which provides the best answer to the question or completes the sentence most satisfactorily.

1 The average annual increase in U.K. real gross domestic product between 1950 and 1980 was approximately

  (a) $2\frac{1}{2}\%$.
  (b) 5%.
  (c) $7\frac{1}{2}\%$.
  (d) 10%.
  (e) $12\frac{1}{2}\%$.

2 The British rate of economic growth ranked in comparison with Belgium, France, Germany and Japan is

  (a) first.
  (b) second.
  (c) third.
  (d) fourth.
  (e) fifth.

3 In the twenty years up to 1980 the standard of living of the British population

  (a) grew at an average annual rate of 1-2%.
  (b) fell at an average annual rate of 1-2%.
  (c) grew at an average annual rate of about 10%.
  (d) fell at an average annual rate of about 10%.
  (e) fell at an unknown rate because productivity and the general price level were increasing rapidly.

4 The annual change in the real value of the national income in the U.K. varied between 1950 and 1980. The (i) maximum and (ii) minimum annual change was

  (a) + 16%.
  (b) + 8%.
  (c) + 2%.
  (d) − 2%.
  (e) − 8%.

5 Approximately what percentage of total personal income has personal disposable income been in the U.K. in recent years?

  (a) 50%.
  (b) 66%.
  (c) 80%.
  (d) 95%.
  (e) 120%.

6 Gross domestic product increased (i) in real terms and (ii) in money terms in the ten years up to 1980 by approximately

  (a) 15-20%.
  (b) 25-50%.
  (c) 75-100%.
  (d) 150-300%.
  (e) 400-500%.

7 What is the approximate percentage addition to or subtraction from U.K. national income at market prices that must be made to arrive at national income at factor cost for recent years?

  (a) + 20 to 40%
  (b) + 10 to 20%
  (c) − 10 to − 20%
  (d) − 10 to − 20%
  (e) None is necessary. They are approximately the same.

8 The allowance for depreciation or capital consumption in the U.K. national accounts in recent years has been approximately what percentage of national income?

(a) 2½%
(b) 10%
(c) 17½%
(d) 25%
(e) 33%

9 Approximately what fraction has net fixed investment been of gross fixed investment in the U.K. in recent years?

(a) a tenth
(b) a quarter
(c) a half to two thirds
(d) two thirds to three quarters
(e) One (i.e. they have been approximately the same)

10 The difference between GNP and GDP for the U.K. in recent years has been that

(a) GNP was about 10% greater than GDP.
(b) GNP was about 10% less than GDP.
(c) GNP was about 25% greater than GDP.
(d) GNP was about 25% less than GDP.
(e) GNP was within approximately 1% of GNP.

11 The value of the multiplier out of national income in the U.K., after allowing for all leakages, is approximately

(a) −2.
(b) 1.5.
(c) 5.
(d) 8.
(e) 10.

12 The source of total savings which grew most rapidly in the U.K. in the 1970s was

(a) persons.
(b) nationalized industries.
(c) companies.
(d) central government.
(e) none of the above. They have all contributed about the same.

13 Which of the following statements about the Gross Capital Stock (real national wealth) of the U.K. is correct?

(a) About 10% consists of dwellings.
(b) About two thirds consists of machinery.
(c) The largest component is the National Debt.
(d) It is about four times the size of the National Income.
(e) It is about half the size of the National Income.

Exercises

Note: Sources are suggested for all exercises. Alternatives may be available if the one mentioned is not in your library. For advice on them and on the collection and presentation of data in tabular and graphical form see pp ix-x.

1 From the Annual Abstract of Statistics make a note of gross national product at current prices, gross domestic product at constant prices and the total U.K. population for the last 10 years. Divide gross domestic product by the total population to obtain figures of GDP per capita. Prepare a graph to show the trends in each of the series: GNP at current prices, GDP at constant prices and GDP per capita over the period.

(i)   Did nominal national income change over the period? If so, by how much?
(ii)   Did real domestic product change over the period? If so, by how much?
(iii) How did the standard of living of the average 'man in the street' change over the period? Would you regard the answer to the previous question as being representative of the population as a whole? Why or why not?

2 Complete the following table for the last 10 years for (a) total personal income, (b) personal disposable income and (c) personal saving.

Year	Total personal income (a)	Personal disposable income (b)	Personal saving (c)	Average propensity to save		Marginal propensity to save	
				(d)	(e)	(f)	(g)
19....							
19....							
19....							
19....							
19....							
19....							
19....							
19....							
19....							
19....							

Source: Annual Abstract of Statistics

(i)   Calculate the average and marginal propensities to save and insert the results in columns (d) and (f). Did you use total personal income or personal disposable income? Why?

(ii) Which varies more, the average or the marginal propensity to save? Why?

(iii) Recalculate the average and marginal propensities to save; but this time relate each year's saving to the previous year's income. Insert the results in columns (e) and (g). Compare these with columns (d) and (f). Which pair would you regard as the more useful for macroeconomic policy?

3 On graph paper prepare a scatter diagram showing the association between consumers' expenditure and personal disposable income for each of the last 10 years. Label each point with a date and join them up. What relationship, if any, does the line you have drawn bear to the consumption function (propensity to consume)?

4 Construct a graph showing for the U.K. for the last 10 years gross national product, total consumption expenditure and total investment expenditure. Which have fluctuated most? Do you think this is normal? Why or why not?

5 Complete the following table showing the values and percentages of gross domestic fixed capital formation accounted for by each of the listed sectors last year and five years previously.

	19....		19....	
	£m	%	£m	%
Persons				
Companies				
Public corporations				
Government				
Total		100%		100%

Source: Annual Abstract of Statistics

(i) Do the figures in the table represent gross investment, net investment or total savings?

(ii) Have the shares of the total accounted for by the different categories changed at all? If so, why?

6 Complete the following table showing the values and shares of total saving accounted for by each of the major sectors last year and 5 years previously.

	19....		19...	
	£m	%	£m	%
Persons				
Companies				
Public corporations				
Central government				
Local government				
		100%		100%

Source: Annual Abstract of Statistics

  (i) What are the main determinants of saving in each category?
 (ii) What changes, if any, occurred in the relative shares of each class of saving? Can you suggest why they may have changed
(iii) Subtract the total saved for each category for the totals invested in exercise 5. Which are net savers and net investors in the two years. Do you think these figures are normal or abnormal? Why?

7 For the most recent and the earliest post-war year for which you can obtain figures, find out the following information from the national accounts and other sources. (Note: <u>Current</u> prices are the changing prices of each year. Figures are also available of certain national income totals revalued by reference to the <u>constant</u> prices of one particular year.)

	19....	19....

(a) Gross national product in current prices
(b) Gross national product in constant prices
(c) Gross domestic product in current prices
(d) Gross domestic fixed capital formation in current prices
(e) Capital consumption in current prices
(f) Net domestic fixed capital formation in current prices
(g) Net national income in current prices
(h) Consumers' expenditure in current prices
(i) Consumers' expenditure in constant prices
(j) Personal income in current prices
(k) Disposable personal income in current prices
(l) Population
(m) Labour force

  (i) Calculate (d) as a percentage of (a) and of (c).
 (ii) Calculate (e) as a percentage of (d).
(iii) Calculate (f) as a percentage of (g).
 (iv) Calculate (h) as a percentage of (a).
  (v) Calculate (i) as a percentage of (b).
 (vi) Calculate (d) per head of the labour force.
(vii) Calculate (g) per head of the population.

Source: Annual Abstract of Statistics

Write a description of the changes that have occurred in the composition of the national income of the U.K. between the two dates. Pay special attention to living standards, productivity and economic growth.

8 Complete the following table for a recent year and another 5 years previously showing the use of gross profits of (listed) companies.

	19....		19....	
	£	%	£	%
Depreciation				
Taxation				
Interest				
Dividends				
Retained profits				
Total		100%		100%

Source: Annual Abstract of Statistics

(i) What is the difference between dividends and interest?

(ii) Give an illustration of what is included in depreciation.

(iii) Has the proportion of the total represented by retained profits altered? If so, can you suggest why? If not, what might cause it to change?

9 The tables at the back of the quarterly National Institute Economic Review include details of the gross national products and private fixed investment of the U.S.A., Japan and Germany as well as for the U.K. Calculate the percentages of GNP going into investment for each country for last year and 10 years previously. Rank them in league tables. What are the causes and the consequences of being at the top or bottom of the table?

Essays

1. Describe the alternative ways in which national income may be estimated and why the resulting figure should be the same regardless of approach.

2. Distinguish between the national income and the national wealth. Are they in any way related?

3. Explain why a country's national income and the standard of living of its people can sometimes move in opposite directions.

4. What difficulties arise in comparing British and French standards of living?

5. What are the relationships between international transactions undertaken by the residents of a country with non-residents and the size of the GNP?

6. Explain carefully the relationship between the average and marginal propensities to save and consume.

7. Distinguish carefully between consumption and investment expenditure. Why is the distinction important in the theory which explains the determination of national income?

8. What are the main determinants of personal saving?

9. What changes in the U.K. economy would increase the propensity to consume?

10. Explain the economic processes which are set in motion when expenditure plans are greater or less than output.

11. Explain why actual savings always equals actual investment but planned savings and investment are equal only when the national income is in equilibrium.

12. Give a graphical account of the multiplier and show why it depends on the marginal propensity to save.

13. What determines the value of the multiplier in the U.K.? What kinds of information do you imagine needs to be collected in order to estimate it?

14. How is the value of the multiplier affected by (a) taxation, (b) exports and imports, and (c) whether investment is autonomous or income-induced?

15. To what extent does the theory of income determination depend on the assumption that savings and investment decisions are made by different persons?

16. Which components of aggregate demand tend to be the most and the least stable over time?

17. What meaning can be attached to the term full employment? If the quantity demanded and the quantity supplied in the labour market are equal, can unemployment still exist?

18. Is thrift a virtue or a vice for the community as a whole?

19. How would the general lengthening of human life after retirement be likely to affect the propensity to consume and the level of income?

20. Does economic theory suggest that business investment is more likely to be affected by the state of business confidence or by the rate of interest?

21. What is the accelerator? How does it help to explain why investment expenditure fluctuates more than consumption? Are there other possible explanations?

22. How far can it be maintained that the growth rate of an economy depends upon its level of investment?

23. What do you think would be the likely effects on total income of a redistribution of income (a) from rich to poor, (b) from persons to companies and (c) from the government to the private sector?

24. Under what circumstances might a rise in the propensity to save lead to less total saving?

25. Compare the effects of a rise in the average propensity to save with a spontaneous rise in the level of investment.

26. The view that hire-purchase is immoral takes hold of the population. Consider the economic effects on the level of income.

27. A machine is invented which more than halves the cost of construction of buildings. Examine its effects on the levels of saving, investment and income. State your assumptions clearly.

28. How might the government try to lower the level of consumption expenditure and raise the level of investment at the same time?

29. Explain why a general cut in wages will not necessarily increase total employment and may have exactly the opposite effect.

30. How does the nature of withdrawals and injections differ between a closed economy with and without an overseas and a government sector?

31. How do booms and slumps spread from country to country?

CHAPTER 6

Money, Banking and the Price Level

The primary concern of economics is with real output. However, the level of production may be influenced by what are called monetary forces. People and institutions choose to hold some of their wealth in the form of real assets and some in money and other financial assets, consisting of claims to wealth, which derive their value from the fact that they provide purchasing power over real goods and services. These forms of wealth can be characterized by their profitability (the income they bring in) and their LIQUIDITY - how quickly and safely they may be converted into cash. Individuals and others hold PORTFOLIOS of assets with varying degrees of liquidity and profitability.

The most perfectly liquid asset is called MONEY and is defined as anything which is generally acceptable for the immediate settlement of debts. Its form can vary. Qualities of divisibility, durability and portability may help money to have its prime characteristic of acceptability. So may support provided by the government as LEGAL TENDER illustrates. Intrinsic worth is inessential. Good money performs the functions of acting as a MEDIUM OF EXCHANGE, a UNIT OF ACCOUNT and as a STORE OF VALUE. A fourth function of providing a STANDARD FOR DEFERRED PAYMENTS is also sometimes mentioned.

There is, of course, both a supply of and demand for money and these play important roles in macroeconomics. It was stated in Chapter 4 that monetary forces affect the rate of interest, especially in the short run. Changes in the quantity of money are also connected with the size of the national income and with the rate of inflation, though the precise nature of the relationships is a matter of major controversy.

The demand for money comes from households and businesses in order to pay for current TRANSACTIONS, as a PRECAUTION against unforeseen circumstances and for SPECULATIVE motives to make capital gains. The last of these is particularly relevant to government fixed-interest securities (BONDS). The price of bonds is inversely related to the rate of interest. Hence if the rate of interest is expected to fall the value of bonds must be expected to rise. Speculators may therefore hold bonds instead of cash. In the reverse case their demand for cash increases. LIQUIDITY PREFERENCE is the term used to describe the desire of the community to hold its wealth in money form, thereby sacrificing interest.

The components of the supply of money consist of coin, notes and, most important, bank deposits which are used for making payments by cheque. Certain other financial assets, such as deposits in savings banks and building societies, are classed as 'near money' in so far as they are highly liquid.

The COMMERCIAL BANKS (sometimes referred to as JOINT-STOCK BANKS) play a key role in the supply of money, which comes about as a direct result of their making credit available to borrowers, thereby creating bank deposits in their favour. The banks are, however, limited in the extent to which they can expand credit by the need to hold some assets in liquid form and because they are liable to control by the CENTRAL BANK. Their portfolios of assets include ADVANCES (or LOANS) which are usually on OVERDRAFT and are the most profitable, INVESTMENTS (comprising medium- and long-term government securities), MONEY AT CALL AND SHORT NOTICE (lent to institutions in The City) and cash itself (consisting of notes, coin and credit balances with the central bank).

The BANK OF ENGLAND is the central bank in the U.K. It has a number of functions, including the issue of bank notes and the management of the NATIONAL DEBT (the sum total of all outstanding government securities) and covering such operations as FUNDING (raising the average maturity of the Debt by selling long-term and buying short-term securities). The principal role of the Bank of England is, however, concerned with operating MONETARY POLICY aimed at influencing the general levels of activity and of prices by regulating the money supply and/or interest rates.

The Bank of England has several methods of trying to do these things. One of its main techniques involves bringing pressure to bear on the commercial banks to encourage or discourage lending to the private sector of the economy by what is known as OPEN MARKET OPERATIONS when the Bank engages in purchases or sales of government securities on the open market. These cause changes in the liquidity of the banks, especially in their cash and deposits at the Bank itself (which comprise so-called HIGH POWERED MONEY, defined as those assets regarded as reserves by the banks). Open market purchases of securities increase the banks' reserves, encouraging credit creation, and vice versa. The volume of the money supply can be measured in several ways. Two of the most common are M_1 (notes, coin and private sector sterling current account deposits) and M_3 (M_1 plus private time, or deposit, accounts and public sector deposits).

There are several other tools in the Bank of England's armoury. However, these are quite often changed and the student is warned to check the latest sources for information on those in current use. Two important policy instruments employed in recent years are (i) Minimum Lending Rate, and (ii) Special Deposits. Minimum Lending Rate (MLR) was for 200 years the rate of interest charged by the Bank of England when lending to financial institutions in its capacity of Lender of Last Resort. Changes in MLR were usually followed by other interest rates, thereby affecting the general demand for money and the amount of bank lending, since loans are only made to willing borrowers. MLR was abandoned in 1981 (except in special circumstances), though the Bank continued to act as lender of last resort without, however, announcing its terms for doing so. Special Deposits are blocked accounts of the commercial banks at the Bank of England. Calls for, or release of, Special Deposits affect bank liquidity and therefore their lending behaviour. A third method of control by the Bank which operated for most of the 1970s was the setting of a minimum reserve asset ratio, whereby certain nominated 'eligible liquid assets' were not allowed to fall below $12\frac{1}{2}$ per cent of 'eligible liabilities' (consisting broadly of total deposits). Finally, there are a miscellaneous set of measures of controlling the quantity of money which have been used in the past. They include persuasion, the setting of ceilings of bank advances and of targets for the growth of deposits (with penalties in the form of compulsory holding of non-interest-bearing Supplementary Deposits, known as 'the corset').

The mechanism by which monetary policy acts on the price level and the volume of output is sometimes viewed through the QUANTITY THEORY OF MONEY. The original form of this theory may be expressed symbolically in the so-called 'equation of exchange' MV = PT, where M is the supply of money, V is the velocity of circulation (the number of times money changes hands on average in a given period, or 1/k, where k is money supply as a fraction of the total value of transactions, i.e. the fraction of the national income the community wishes to hold in cash), P is the general price level, or the average price per unit of output, and T is the volume of transactions. (It might be worth adding that the relationships summarized in the equation MV = PT have been expressed in slightly different forms as MV = PQ and MV = PY, where Q and Y stand for the quantity, or real value, of output.) The equation suggests that a change in M will be accompanied by a change in P in the same direction if V and T are constant. That is the basis for the view associated with the Monetarist school of thought that inflation is due to increases in the supply of money. Since it is known that V (and T) can fluctuate in the short run, a modern reformulation of the quantity theory incorporates changes in the real money supply (i.e. its purchasing power) and in interest rates (nominal rates adjusted for inflation) and is based on the predictability of V (and T) to reach similar conclusions.

The relevance of the quantity theory to macroeconomic policy is an extremely controversial matter. The equation of exchange is a truism which does not imply causal relationships. Hence it can be a matter of debate whether changes in the quantity of money cause changes in income or whether the causal link runs in the opposite direction (with changes in income causing changes in the quantity of money). The existence of the controversy reflects the fact that there is a disagreement about exactly how the economy works and what are the main determinants of spending behaviour. These may well differ at different times (e.g. in depressions, booms and periods of rapid inflation). Morever there are important time lags involved in the effectiveness of monetary policy since it is generally recognized that output reacts much more quickly to reductions in the quantity of money than does the general price level (implying that an anti-inflation monetary policy causes output to fall before it brings down the rate of inflation).

Monetary policy works primarily through the banks and its effectiveness is threatened by the existence of non-banking financial institutions (including 'secondary' and 'fringe' banks) such as insurance companies and building societies which provide loans of one sort or another to households and businesses. A further constraint on monetary policy is the other activities of the government, whose need to borrow to finance some of its expenditure is shown by the size of the PUBLIC SECTOR BORROWING REQUIREMENT (PSBR). This may affect the liquidity of the banks and total spending.

INFLATION is a prime target of monetary policy. Inflation may be defined in several ways but it is characterized by a tendency for the general price level to rise (though actual prices may be held down or suppressed by restraint or controls). The pace of inflation is measured by means of price INDEX NUMBERS. One year is chosen as the base and the index compares the average price level in each year as a percentage of that in the base year. The averages are weighted by the importance of each good or service in total expenditure. Practical problems abound in the construction of price index numbers, including the need to make allowances for quality changes and the choice of weights, especially over long periods and when prices are changing rapidly.

Inflation is particularly likely when aggregate demand increases at levels of national income at, or close to, full employment. Analysis employing aggregate supply curves may throw further light on the matter. Until fairly recent times there was thought to be a relationship between inflation and unemployment, exhibited in the so-called PHILLIPS CURVE, which implied a TRADE-OFF between them — lower inflation being obtainable at the cost of higher unemployment. Experience has, however, shown that inflation can accompany high unemployment in periods of STAGFLATION, when stagnant and even falling output coexists with sharp increases in the general price level. The reasons for this are disputed. One explanation stresses the importance of expectations of future changes in the price level as it is argued that workers bargain for real rather than for money wages.

Phillips curve analysis has been extended to illustrate this thoery. Since the relationships between inflation and unemployment originally shown in the first Phillips curve no longer hold, it has been suggested that they were in fact applicable to short-run situations corresponding to the expectations of inflation of the times. Sets of short-run curves can be constructed, each of which is appliable to a different expected level of inflation (known as EXPECTATIONS AUGMENTED PHILLIPS CURVES) and implying also a long-run Phillips curve associated with a concept of a NATURAL RATE OF UNEMPLOYMENT (the minimum level of, mainly structural, unemployment attainable in the long run). Such analysis may be used to demonstrate continuous, and even accelerating inflation when trade unions bargain over real rather than money wages and when aggregate demand is maintained at a level designed to keep unemployment below the 'natural rate'.

It must again be stressed that this is a major controversial area in economics. The part played by changes in the quantity of money in the inflationary process and the role of monetary policy are hotly debated. Attempts to validate alternative theories remain inconclusive. Economists of the Monetarist school of thought favour reliance on monetary policy. Those of the school known as Keynesian do not deny its importance but believe in the use also of <u>fiscal policy</u> (and at times prices and incomes policies (see p. 129).

ANALYSIS

Multiple Choice

Choose the alternative which provides the best answer to the question or completes the sentence most satisfactorily.

1 Legal tender is the name used to describe

  (a) any object legally used as money in a country.
  (b) banknotes where they are in legal circulation.
  (c) money which cannot legally be refused in settlement of a debt.
  (d) the legally approved form of payment used for the settlement of international transactions.
  (e) non-counterfeit notes or coin.

2 Each of the following is a recognized function of money, with one exception. Which is it?

  (a) To serve as a unit of account
  (b) To bring about the double coincidence of wants
  (c) To assist exchange and specialization
  (d) To act as a standard for deferred payments
  (e) To be used as a store of value

3 Which of the following characteristics is <u>essential</u> for a financial asset to possess if it is to be used as money?

  (a) Acceptability
  (b) Durability
  (c) Divisibility
  (d) Intrinsic value
  (e) Portability

4 The National Debt consists of

  (a) domestic assets owned by non-residents.
  (b) the sum by which imports exceed exports.
  (c) the sums borrowed by the government to pay for wars.
  (d) the liabilities of nationalized industries.
  (e) the total financial liabilities of the government.

5 Liquid assets are those which are

  (a) lent to financial institutions.
  (b) lent to non-residents.
  (c) easily and speedily exchangeable for other assets.
  (d) easily and speedily exchangeable for cash.
  (e) guaranteed a safe return of interest.

6 Which is the most liquid of the following financial assets held by an individual?

  (a) An insurance policy
  (b) A credit balance in a building society account
  (c) Credit standing in a current account in a bank
  (d) A loan made to a brother for 6 weeks
  (e) Unused current postage stamps

7 Which of the following reasons illustrate (i) the transactions demand for money and (ii) the speculative demand for money?

  (a) The desire for a reserve in case of illness
  (b) The desire for money to pay fares for a journey to work
  (c) The desire for cash to make a venture in government securities
  (d) The desire to provide a reserve against an increase in the rate of inflation
  (e) The desire to cover a risk that a new business may not be successful

8 If the market rate of interest goes up then there will be an automatic

    (a) fall in the value of money.
    (b) fall in the price of bonds.
    (c) fall in the real value of wages.
    (d) increase in the demand for money.
    (e) increase in the supply of money.

9 Which of the following is a liability of commercial banks?

    (a) Current account deposits
    (b) Government securities
    (c) Special deposits at the Bank of England
    (d) Treasury bills
    (e) Money lent at short notice

10 Which is the least liquid of the following assets of a commercial bank?

    (a) Treasury bills
    (b) Securities
    (c) Loans made on overdraft
    (d) Special deposits
    (e) Call money

11 Hypothetica has a single commercial bank which keeps 8% of its assets in gold and lends the rest to customers. Its holdings of gold are £1000. What will be the size of its total liabilities if it lends up to its maximum?

    (a) £80 000
    (b) £18 000
    (c) £12 500
    (d) £10 800
    (e) £10 000

12 If a bank discounts a bill of exchange worth £100 in 3 months' time for £97 the discount rate would be

    (a) 3%
    (b) 12%
    (c) 97%
    (d) 100%
    (e) None of the above. It would be determined by the market of interest.

13 Which of the following would tend to cause commercial banks to increase their total deposits?

    (a) A call by the Bank of England for special deposits
    (b) A sale of Treasury bills to the commercial banks by the Bank of England
    (c) A purchase of Treasury bills from the discount houses by the Bank of England
    (d) An increase in the period Treasury bills must be held to reach maturity
    (e) A rise in Minimum Lending Rate

14 When the Bank of England raises Minimum Lending Rate, the rates charged by building societies for loans may remain unchanged because

    (a) they are legally exempted from the need to do so by the government for social reasons.
    (b) they are given a special tax concession by law.
    (c) the source of their funds may not be affected by the Bank's lending rate.
    (d) competition among them prevents any increase in charges.
    (e) they do not want to lose business.

15 If the Bank of England adopts an expansionist open market operations policy, this means that it will

    (a) sell securities on the open market.
    (b) offer the commercial banks more credit on the open market.
    (c) openly announce to the market that it intends to expand credit.
    (d) buy securities from non-government holders.
    (e) open its doors to borrowers at less than its minimum lending rate.

16 High-powered money is the term used to describe

(a) money lent at high rates of interest.
(b) money lent by banks to businesses which have a rapid turnover.
(c) the total deposits of commercial banks.
(d) assets which are regarded as reserves by the commercial banks.
(e) banknotes which have a high velocity of circulation.

17 Which of the following policies is appropriate for a central bank to adopt during a credit squeeze?

(a) Trying to force down interest rates
(b) Lowering the commercial banks' reserve ratios of liquid assets
(c) Trying to persuade the commercial banks to increase overdrafts to their customers
(d) Releasing balances standing to the credit of the commercial banks which are frozen in accounts at the central bank
(e) Open market selling of government securities

18 If the Bank of England buys Treasury bills and sells new government bonds it is engaged in

(a) open market operations.
(b) funding.
(c) credit creation.
(d) acting as Lender of Last Resort.
(e) discounting.

19 According to the quantity thoery of money

(a) prices vary in direct proportion to the velocity of circulation of money.
(b) MP = TV.
(c) the supply of and demand for money determine the rate of interest.
(d) the supply of and demand for money determine the price level.
(e) the supply of money is determined by the quantity of it in existence.

20 Assume a closed economy with no government and a money stock of $5 million. The national income is $10 million. The velocity of circulation is

(a) impossible to know without information about the general price level.
(b) impossible to know without information about the general price level and the volume of transactions.
(c) $\frac{1}{2}$.
(d) 2.
(e) 50.

21 If an increase in the quantity of money does not cause an increase in the general price level during a slump, this is most likely because

(a) the number of times a unit of money is used goes up instead.
(b) the kinds of money increased are not legal tender.
(c) the volume of transactions decreases in exactly the same proportion as the quantity of money increases.
(d) people decide to hold larger cash balances.
(e) inflation occurs instead.

22 Which of the following actions by the government would be the most likely to lead to a decrease in the quantity of money?

(a) Lowering taxes
(b) Increasing government expenditure
(c) Instructing the Mint to manufacture more coins
(d) Instructing the Mint to print more banknotes
(e) Instructing the Bank of England to buy government securities from the public

23 Inflationary pressure cannot exist if

(a) prices do not increase.
(b) inflation is caused by cost push.
(c) inflation is caused by demand pull.
(d) the economy is not at full employment.
(e) None of the above.

24 Inflation in a country is likely to

(a)   redistribute wealth from debtors to creditors.
(b)   stimulate investment in 'collectables'.
(c)   lead to hyperinflation.
(d)   cause the nominal rate of interest to fall.
(e)   raise the purchasing power of domestic currency over foreign currencies.

25 A reasonably reliable sign that suppressed inflation exists in an economy is that

(a)   businesses charge lower prices than they could for the products that they sell.
(b)   people choose to hold larger balances at the bank.
(c)   prices are increasing.
(d)   people resort to barter.
(e)   the economy is at full employment.

26 The real money supply consists of

(a)   the nominal money supply deflated by a price index.
(b)   current account deposits at commercial banks.
(c)   deposit account deposits at commercial banks.
(d)   current and deposit account deposits at commercial banks.
(e)   current and deposit account deposits at commercial banks plus notes and coin in circulation.

27 If the money rate of interest is 15% at a time when prices rise by 20%, the marginal real rate of return on investment is

(a)   −15% or higher.
(b)   −5% or higher.
(c)   +5% or higher.
(d)   +15% or higher.
(e)   +20% or higher.

28 A Phillips curve shows the relationship between

(a)   unemployment rates and the level of prices.
(b)   unemployment rates and the rate of inflation.
(c)   unemployment rates and the size of the national income.
(d)   unemployment rates and changes in the expected rate of inflation.
(e)   changes in wage rates and changes in the rate of inflation.

29

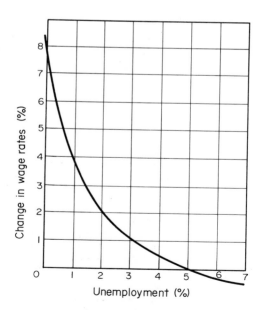

Fig. 6.1

Fig. 6.1 shows the relationship between changes in money wage rates and unemployment (per cent) for a hypothetical economy which enjoys an annual productivity increase of 4%.   (i) What change in wage rates is compatible with zero unemployment? (ii) What rate of unemployment is compatible with stable money wage rates? (iii) What rate of unemployment is compatible with a stable price level? (Assume the curve does not shift position.)

(a) 1%
(b) 2%
(c) 4%
(d) 5%
(e) 8%

30 A rightward shift of a Phillips curve could be due to

(a) a fall in the rate of inflation.
(b) a rise in interest rates.
(c) a fall in the quantity of money.
(d) expectations of a fall in unemployment.
(e) expectations of a rise in the rate of inflation.

31 The natural rate of unemployment is the term used to describe

(a) the level of unemployment compatible with price stability.
(b) the maximum level of short-run frictional unemployment.
(c) the maximum level of unemployment at the bottom of a slump.
(d) the minimum level of unemployment at the top of a boom.
(e) the sum of frictional, seasonal, structural and cyclical unemployment.

32 Price index numbers are designed to measure

(a) the absolute level of prices of goods and services.
(b) the real value of goods and services consumed.
(c) changes in the volume of output.
(d) changes in the cost or value of production.
(e) changes in living standards.

33 Spiralia experienced an increase in the value of its national income last year of 50%. Prices additionally went up by a quarter. Spiralian real income went up therefore by

(a) 20%.
(b) 25%.
(c) 75%.
(d) 120%.
(e) 125%.

34 A family spends 60% of its income on food and 40% on clothing. The price of food goes up by 20% and that of clothing by 5%. The weighted average price index rises by

(a) $12\frac{1}{2}$%.
(b) 14%.
(c) 15%.
(d) 25%.
(e) 40%.

35 Smith, Brown and Jones spend their income as follows:

	Food (%)	Clothing (%)	Other goods (%)
Smith	20	20	60
Brown	30	20	50
Jones	35	20	45

The price of food has risen by 10%, the price of clothing has fallen by 7% and the price of other goods has risen on average by 15%. Which of the following is true?

(a) Jones has had the biggest increase in the cost of living.
(b) Brown's cost of living has not changed.
(c) Smith's and Jones's cost of living have both risen by the same amount.
(d) Smith has had the smallest increase in the cost of living.
(e) The cost of living has risen most for Smith and least for Jones.

36 The national income of Numismatia has doubled since the year dot. <u>Ceteris paribus</u>, which of the following circumstances would preclude the conclusion being drawn that the standard of living of Numismatian inhabitants has at least doubled?

(a) The population has fallen.
(b) The quality of goods has improved.
(c) People are buying bread instead of baking their own.
(d) The price level has fallen.
(e) All of the above.

37 Which of the following non-banking financial institutions is likely to feel the first impact of a change in Minimum Lending Rate?

(a) Insurance companies
(b) Discount houses
(c) Building societies
(d) Issuing houses
(e) Unit trusts

38 The function of an accepting house is to

(a) discount Treasury bills.
(b) provide the premises in which banks can discount bills of exchange.
(c) guarantee bills of exchange against the risk of default.
(d) accept bills of exchange in return for Treasury bills.
(e) act as a standard for deferred payments.

39 An individual is considering buying some financial assets. The general price level is assumed to be relatively stable. Which of the following would he normally be able to expect to have (i) the highest and (ii) the lowest yield prospects?

(a) Ordinary shares in a range of small private companies
(b) Preference shares in a range of medium-sized companies
(c) Debentures in large corporations
(d) Undated government securities
(e) Treasury bills

Problems

1 The National Scarecrow Bank Ltd is the only commercial bank in Liquidania and has the following balance sheet:

Liabilities	£	Assets	£
Deposits	500	Cash	40
		Bills	160
		Loans	300
	———		———
	£500		£500
	———		———

(i) A customer pays in £100 of gold, and the immediate balance sheet position becomes:

Liabilities	£	Assets	£

(ii) What is its cash ratio now?

(iii) The bank then expands credit to its legal maximum, which is an 8% cash ratio. Its balance sheet is now:

Liabilities	£	Assets	£

(iv) The central bank now requires the bank to restore its 40% liquid asset ratio. No further bills are assumed to be available. The balance sheet is now:

Liabilities	£	Assets	£

(v) Assume that there are now two commercial banks, each of which has half of total deposits. A customer of the N.S.B. Ltd leaves the country after withdrawing £20 in gold. What reduction in loans should the bank make to restore its original 40% liquid asset ratio?

2

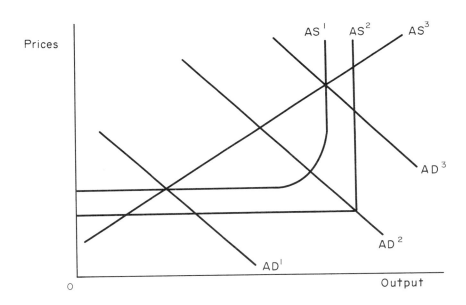

Fig. 6.2

Fig. 6.2 shows three aggregate supply curves and three positions of an aggregate demand curve.

(i) Which of the supply curves suggest that full employment is reached abruptly and simultaneously in all sectors of the economy?
(ii) What is full employment output in (i)?
(iii) Which supply curve suggests that full employment is reached after a 'bottleneck' stage?
(iv) Which supply curve does not give any indication of when full employment is reached?
(v) Aggregate demand increases from AD^1 to AD^2.
    (a) With which supply curve will output increase most?
    (b) With which supply curve will prices rise most?
(vi) Aggregate demand increases from AD^2 to AD^3.
    (a) With which supply curve will output increase most?
    (b) With which supply curve will prices rise most??
(vii) Which supply curve offers no scope for expanding output without causing inflation?
(viii) Which supply curve offers most scope for expanding output without causing inflation?
(ix) Which supply curve offers most scope for inflation without expanding output?
(x) Which supply curve offers most support for Monetarist policies?
(xi) Which supply curve offers most support for Keynesian policies?

3 The following balance sheets show all the assets and liabilities of a central bank, and the combined joint-stock banks in Mythica.

Central bank				Joint-stock banks			
	£m		£m		£m		£m
Bankers' a/cts	6 000	Securities	7 000	Deposit a/cts	20 000	Notes and coins	4 000
Public a/cts	4 000	Discounts and advances	5 000	Current a/cts	80 000	Cash at central bank	6 000
Other a/cts	2 000					Money at call	10 000
						Bills discounted	5 000
						Investments	25 000
						Advances	50 000
	12 000		12 000		100 000		100 000

Complete the following balance sheets to show the position after the sale by the central bank of £1000 of securities to the general public. Assume that a liquid asset ratio of 25% must be maintained and that the public keep 20% of their credit balances with the banks on deposit account.

Central bank				Joint-stock banks			
	£m		£m		£m		£m

4 The following information is known about the economy of Emvypetia. The total money supply is £200. Every pound is used twice a year. The average general level of prices is £4. Use the quantity theory of money to answer the following. (Each question is to be regarded as quite separate from the others.)

 (i)   What is T?
 (ii) There is an increase in the quantity of money of £50. V and T are unchanged. What is the average price level?
 (iii) The money supply increases by 25%. What is the percentage change in the price level if V and T are constant?
 (iv) The quantity of money is increased by 25%. Prices and the volume of output are unchanged. What is the value of V?
 (v)   There is a 50% fall in the velocity of circulation but output and the price level have not changed. How much must the money supply have altered?
 (vi) T rises by 80%, M rises by 50%, V falls by 25%. What is P?
 (vii) There is a 10% fall in M, while V is unchanged. What is the value of the national output?

5 The national income of Sophistria went up from £200 million last year to £400 million this year. (Each question is quite separate from the others.)

 (i)   Calculate the value of the national income this year as a percentage of last year's.
 (ii) Prices went up over the year by a quarter. How much did the real value of the national income change?
 (iii) The price index for this year, using last year as the base, is 250. What is the index number of the value of real national income on the same base?
 (iv) The index of the real value of the national income on last year's base is 160. What is the price index number for this year on the same base?
 (v)   The real value of national income has gone up by 50% since last year. How much have prices risen on average?
 (vi) The real value of the national income has quadrupled since last year. What is the price index for this year based on last?

6

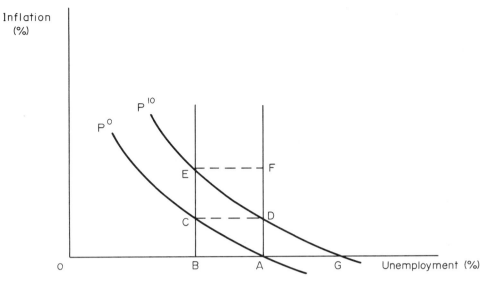

Fig. 6.3

Fig. 6.3 shows two short-run Phillips curves (expectations-augmented) P^0 and P^{10} corresponding to expected rates of inflation of zero and 10%.

(i)   What is the long-run level of unemployment?
(ii)   What is the long-run Phillips curve?
(iii)   What is the 'natural' rate of unemployment?
(iv)   Suppose unemployment is OA and it is official policy to change it to OB. How might this be achieved?
(v)   Following (iv), if unemployment became OB as a result of government policy, what would be the immediate effect on the rate of inflation?
(vi)   Following (v), what would happen to the short-run Phillips curve?
(vii)   Following (vi), what would happen to the rate of unemployment?
(viii) If government policy were to hold the level of unemployment at OB, what would be the long-run rate of inflation?
(ix)   If inflation is proceeding at a steady 10% and expected to remain at the same rate, what would be the long-run level of unemployment?
(x)   Where would a P^{20} short-run Phillips curve corresponding to an expected inflation rate of 20% cross the vertical long run Phillips curve?

U.K. ECONOMY

Multiple Choice

Choose the alternative which provides the best answer to the question or completes the sentence most satisfactorily.

1 Which of the following are components of the definitions of the money supply known as sterling (i) M1 and (ii) M3?

1. Coin and notes
2. Sterling current account deposits of the private sector
3. Sterling deposit account deposits of the private sector
4. Sterling current account deposits of the public sector
5. Sterling deposit account deposits of the public sector

(a)   1 and 2 only
(b)   2 and 3 only
(c)   1,2 and 4 only
(d)   2,3,4 and 5 only
(e)   1,2,3,4 and 5

2 In the twenty years up to 1980 the money supply grew at approximately the same rate as

   (a) the rate of interest.
   (b) the deficit on the balance of payments.
   (c) the real national income.
   (d) the general level of prices.
   (e) real investment.

3 The short-term debt of the British Government is known as

   (a) the National Debt.
   (b) Consols.
   (c) Special Deposits.
   (d) the Public Sector Borrowing Requirement.
   (e) Treasury bills.

4 Domestic credit expansion is a measure of

   (a) the money supply, M1.
   (b) the change in the money supply, M3.
   (c) the change in the money supply, sterling M3.
   (d) the change in the money supply, sterling M3, adjusted for external finance of the balance of
        payments.
   (e) the change in the money supply, sterling M3, adjusted for the Public Sector Borrowing
        Requirement.

5 What was the annual average rate of inflation in the U.K. during the period (i) 1950-60,
(ii) 1960-70 and (iii) 1970-80?

   (a) $2\frac{1}{2}$%
   (b) 4%
   (c) 15%
   (d) 25%
   (e) 35%

6 Evidence on the relationship between rates of unemployment and rates of change of the general
price level in the 1970s and early 1980s suggests that the rate of inflation that was associated
with an unemployment rate of about $2\frac{1}{2}$% was

   (a) approximately 2%.
   (b) approximately 5%.
   (c) approximately 10%.
   (d) approximately 20%.
   (e) variable between 5 and 30%.

7 In calculating the retail price index government statisticians use a 'weighted average'. The
weights in recent years for (i) food and (ii) transport and vehicles were approximately

   (a) 50 (out of a total of 1000).
   (b) 150 (out of a total of 1000).
   (c) 200 (out of a total of 1000).
   (d) 300 (out of a total of 1000).
   (e) 350 (out of a total of 1000).

8 In which of the following periods was the general (%) unemployment level (i) highest and (ii)
lowest?

   (a) 1930-35
   (b) 1960-65
   (c) 1965-70
   (d) 1970-75
   (e) 1975-80

9 In which of the following periods was the average annual rate of inflation (i) highest and
(ii) lowest?

   (a) 1930-35
   (b) 1950-55
   (c) 1960-65
   (d) 1970-75
   (e) 1975-80

10 All but one of the following are functions of commercial banks. Which is the exception?

(a) Lending to private customers
(b) Making profits
(c) Giving investment advice
(d) Lending money at call and short notice to the Bank of England
(e) Buying government securities

11 Which of the following is (i) the largest and (ii) the least profitable group of assets of the commercial banks?

(a) Balances at the Bank of England
(b) Government securities
(c) Loans and advances
(d) Money at call and short notice
(e) Treasury bills and other bills of exchange

12 Frozen assets of the commercial banks at the Bank of England are known as

(a) government securities.
(b) tied loans.
(c) public sector accounts.
(d) special deposits.
(e) liquid assets.

13 The proportion of the note issue covered by holdings of gold in the Issue Department of the Bank of England is approximately

(a) less than 1%.
(b) 8%.
(c) 10%.
(d) 25%.
(e) 100%.

14 All but one of the following are functions of the Bank of England. Which is the exception?

(a) Acting as a lender of last resort
(b) Managing the National Debt
(c) Buying and selling government securities
(d) Controlling the issue of notes
(e) Minting coins for circulation

15 Which of the following has/have been used by the Bank of England as instruments of monetary policy in the last twenty years?

1. Selling government securities to the commercial banks
2. Changing the reserve asset ratios of the commercial banks
3. Stipulating a minimum reserve asset ratio
4. Freezing assets of the commercial banks
5. Setting targets for bank lending

(a) 1,2 and 4 only
(b) 2,4 and 5 only
(c) 3,4 and 5 only
(d) 1,3,4 and 5 only
(e) 1,2,3,4 and 5

16 Which THREE of the following hold the largest assets?

1. Building societies
2. Finance houses
3. Insurance companies
4. Investment trusts
5. National Savings
6. Pension funds
7. Unit trusts

(a) 1,3 and 6 only
(b) 1,5 and 7 only
(c) 2,3 and 5 only
(d) 2,4 and 7 only
(e) 3,4 and 6 only

17 The bulk of the funds of building societies are lent to

(a) builders.
(b) local authorities for house construction.
(c) joint-stock companies.
(d) private housing associations.
(e) the general public.

18 A 'bear' on the Stock Exchange is a

(a) speculator who applies for new issues of shares in the hope that the price will go up.
(b) speculator who buys shares in the hope that the price will go up.
(c) dealer member of the Stock Exchange.
(d) speculator whose holdings of the shares in a company is so large that selling them would affect the market price.
(e) speculator who sells shares which he does not possess.

19 Which of the following would be the most appropriate to deal with if you wish to buy £1000 worth of shares in I.C.I. Ltd?

(a) A bill broker
(b) A stockbroker
(c) A stockjobber
(d) A merchant banker
(e) The company secretary of I.C.I. Ltd

20 With which of the following economists do you most associate the term 'monetarist'?

(a) Milton Friedman
(b) J.M. Keynes
(c) R.G. Lipsey
(d) P. Samuelson
(e) Adam Smith

Exercises

Note: Sources are suggested for all exercises. Alternatives may be available if the one mentioned is not in your library. For advice on them and on the collection and presentation of data in tabular and graphical form see pp ix-x.

1 Complete the following table which gives details of various components of the money supply and Gross National Product for a recent year and another 5 to 10 years previously. (N.B. Current and deposit accounts are also known as sight and time deposits respectively.)

		19....	19....
1	Notes and coin		
2	Private sector and sterling sight deposits		
3	Private sector sterling time deposits		
4	Public sector sterling deposits		
5	Money supply: sterling M1 (1+2)		
6	Money supply: sterling M3 (5+3+4)		
7	GNP		
8	Domestic credit expansion (DCE)		
9	Public sector borrowing reqt (PSBR)		

Source: Annual Abstract of Statistics

(i) Calculate sterling M1 and M3 as percentages of GNP. Have they risen or fallen? Do these percentages tell you anything about the velocity of circulation?
(ii) What is the relationship, if any, between (a) domestic credit expansion, (b) the public sector borrowing requirement and measures of the supply of money?
(iii) List the various ways in which the government may try to control the components of the money supply in the table.

2 Using data from the <u>Annual Abstract of Statistics</u> prepare two bar charts showing the distribution of the assets of the commercial banks at a recent date and another one to two years earlier. Distinguish the following categories of asset.

    1. Notes and coin and balances at the Bank of England
    2. Money at call and short notice
    3. Bills of exchange and Treasury bills
    4. Special deposits
    5. Government securities
    6. Advances
    7. Total assets

  (i) Calculate 1 and (1+2+3) as percentages of 7 for each year. What meaning do you attach to these percentages? Have they changed between the two dates. If so, what does that signify?
 (ii) Rank the assets according to (a) their liquidity and (b) their profitability. Have the rank orders changed between the two dates? If so, why; if not, why not?
(iii) Over which groups of assets do the banks have least control in the short run?

3 Collect figures from the <u>Annual Abstract of Statistics</u> of real output (GDP at constant prices) and of the average price level (the Index of Retail Prices) for each of the last five years. Plot the two series on graph paper. Calculate the purchasing power of the pound over the period by taking the reciprocal of the price index (i.e. divide the index for each year into one). Plot the purchasing power of the pound on the same graph. What connections are there between the three series? Are any of them likely to be <u>causal</u>? Identify any years of accelerating and decelerating rates of inflation.

4 From the <u>Annual Abstract of Statistics</u> extract figures of (a) the Retail Price Index and (b) sterling M1 for the last 10 years. Calculate the percentage changes in (a) and (b) from each year to the next.

    Prepare a scatter diagram showing the relationship between the two series, using the horizontal axis for M1 and the vertical axis for prices. Plot points showing the associated changes in the price level and the money supply in the same year, label each with a date. Inspect the scatter of points. Do they seem to be correlated? Now plot a second set of points using a coloured pencil and indicating the change in the price level associated with the money supply in the <u>previous</u> year. Do these points show a higher degree of correlation than the first set? Why might they be expected to do so?

Can any of the correlations shown in the diagrams be regarded as indicating <u>causal</u> relationships. If so, why and which variable do you think determines which? (Be careful! <u>This</u> is not an easy question.)

5 Using the series showing the changes in the price level calculated for the previous exercises and figures of the percentage unemployment rate for the same years, prepare another scatter diagram substituting the latter for sterling M1. What relationship does the scatter of points have to the Phillips curve(s)? Is the correlation between these two series better or worse than that between the two series of exercise 4? If you had used data relating to a period prior to the Second World War, would you expect to have found a higher or lower correlation?

6 Find out the total deposits (or accumulated funds) of the following financial institutions in a recent year. Calculate the changes in each over the previous year to complete the final column in the table.

	£m	Change over previous year
Commercial banks)		
Building societies) total deposits		
Trustee savings banks)		
National Savings)		
Hire purchase debt)		
Superannuation funds) accumulated funds		
Life assurance companies)		

Source: Annual Abstract of Statistics

  (i) Rank each column according to size.
 (ii) Which are conventionally included in the money supply?
(iii) Which have been increasing in relative importance in recent years? Can you suggest any reasons for this?

7 From the <u>Bank of England Quarterly Bulletin</u> (or the <u>Midland Bank Review</u>) make a note of the dates when the Bank of England changed the amount of special deposits that the commercial banks were required to hold. Can you find any evidence that there was any following change in the rate of increase or decrease of total bank deposits? Then make a list of the dates when the Bank changed its Minimum Lending Rate. Did total bank deposits alter following changes in MLR? What are the significance of your findings for the effectiveness of monetary policy?

8 Find out the market rates of interest payable one day last week on each of the following assets?

>   A deposit account with a 'high street' bank
>   A building society share account (gross before tax)
>   An index-linked 'granny bond' National Savings certificate
>   A Treasury bill
>   A deposit at the Trustee Savings Bank
> $2\frac{1}{2}$% Consols

- (i) Why do the rates of interest you have found differ?
- (ii) How easy is it for an investor to switch funds between the various assets in the short run?
- (iii) Find out the increase in the Retail Price Index last year. If you had held each of these assets for 12 months, what <u>real</u> rate of interest would you have earned on them? Are any of the rates negative? Why should anyone wish, or be prepared, to hold an asset which yields a negative rate of return?
- (iv) How do the yields compare with those on debentures, preference and ordinary shares sold on the Stock Exchange?

(Sources: <u>Financial Times</u>, <u>The Times</u> (Business pages), <u>Annual Abstract of Statistics</u> and personal enquiries.)

9 Estimate the proportion of your family expenditure and the average of that of all members of your class on the following groups of goods. Compare these with the weights used by the Department of Employment for the calculation of the Retail Price Index. Find the percentage changes that took place in the price level for each group of goods between two dates, one of which should be recent and the other as long ago as you can trace. Calculate three price index numbers using the three sets of weights. (Multiply each price change by its appropriate weight as shown in columns (e), (f) and (g) of the following table, and divide the sum of each of these columns by 1000 – the sum of the weights.)

	Weights			% Price change 19.... to 19....	(a)×(d)	(b)×(d)	(c)×(d)
	D of E	Your family	Class average				
	(a)	(b)	(c)	(d)	(e)	(f)	(g)
Food							
Drink (alcoholic)							
Tobacco							
Housing							
Fuel and light							
Durable household goods							
Clothing and footwear							
Transport and vehicles							
Miscellaneous goods							
Services							
All goods and services	1000	1000	1000				

Source: Annual Abstract of Statistics

- (i) Which index number shows the highest and the lowest average price change. Can you explain why?
- (ii) If money incomes did not change over the period, who gained or lost, relatively speaking, in living standards, your family or the rest of the class?
- (iii) Why, in reality, might your answer to (ii) above be misleading?

10 Prepare a list of a 'basket' of groceries costing about £30 and find out their prices in the cheapest shopping centre of your city. Obtain the prices of similar goods in your home district. Prepare a price index for your area using the other area as base, and one of the sets of weights used in exercise 9 above.

Essays

1. Why do modern coins have values in excess of that of their metallic content? Would they perform money's functions better if they did not?

2. 'The main difference between money and other financial assets is that it is the only one that does not earn any interest.' Is this a good and full explanation of the meaning of money?

3. Can the motives behind the demand for money be related to the standard functions that money is said to perform?

4. What is the difference between 'money' and 'credit'?

5. 'If the conventional forms of money are restricted in supply by law other money substitutes will take their place.' Assess the validity of this statement.

6. 'The best way of grouping financial assets is according to their liquidity.' Discuss this view with reference to the assets of banks.

7. To what extent is it true that liquidity and profitability are conflicting aims for a commercial bank?

8. Describe the process of credit creation in a country with a single commercial bank.

9. Consider the view that the British banking system is possible only because most people do not realize that the banks could not possibly pay all their customers in full at any one time.

10. Consider the implications for the commercial banks of a spontaneous desire by business and the general public to hold larger current accounts and smaller deposit accounts.

11. Consider the implications of a law which required the Bank of England to pay 1% interest per annum to holders of five pound notes.

12. Compare and contrast the functions of the Bank of England with those the commercial banks.

13. How and why do the authorities try to control the supply of credit?

14. Why is it sometimes said that monetary policy is more effective as a device for contracting than for expanding credit?

15. Explain why the total value of notes in circulation appears as a liability of the Bank of England.

16. How can the Bank of England's function of 'lender of last resort' assist in the operation of monetary policy?

17. Discuss the implications for monetary policy of a significant increase in government borrowing through the issue of Treasury bills.

18. Does an increase in the quantity of money cause inflation? Always?

19. 'At levels of national income below full employment an increase in aggregate demand raises output. At levels above this the effect is seen in the general price level.' Discuss.

20. Is inflation better described as a tendency for the general price level to rise or as an excess of aggregate demand over aggregate supply?

21. Outline the most likely effects of inflation upon the distribution of income.

22. If prices double overnight while the national income also doubles, does this mean that everybody is in exactly the same economic position?

23. What links are there between inflation on the one hand and costs, demand and productivity on the other?

24. What part do expectations play in the inflationary process?

25. What is meant by a negative rate of interest. How can it come about?

26. Is there a 'trade-off' between inflation and unemployment?

27. What relationships are depicted in a Phillips curve? What explanations can be given for its shifting to the right?

28. How is the rate of inflation affected by whether workers bargain for real rather than for money wage increases?

29. Is inflation the scourge of our times?

30. Imagine that the index of retail prices has risen by 5% since last year, but your cost of living has increased by only 2%. Give as many explanations of the difference as you can think of.

31. Explain what is meant by discounting a bill of exchange.

32. 'The Stock Exchange is a market for old securities. It does not really help to raise new capital for industry.' Discuss.

33. What are the chief non-banking financial institutions? What principally distinguishes them from commercial banks?

34. What is the public sector borrowing requirement? On what does its size depend?

35. How does a government budget surplus or deficit affect the quantity of money?

CHAPTER 7

International Trade

The analysis of international trade involves, in essence, no more than the application of general principles of economics. The subject usually merits separate treatment, however, for two main reasons, both of which arise from the existence of national boundaries. The first is that factors of production tend to be much more mobile within countries than between them. The second is that a national frontier enables a government to legislate on matters affecting its own economic life with some freedom. It is almost universal practice for a country to have its own currency. That of the U.K. is, for example, pounds sterling, while the currency of the U.S.A. is dollars. This implies that British and American traders require pounds to buy each other's goods and raises the question of EXCHANGE RATES, the prices of national currencies in terms of each other (see below).

It is probably not too misleading to approach international economics initially from one of two standpoints: (1) microeconomic, stressing resource allocation, and (2) macroeconomic, stressing finance. The allocation aspect involves extending the theory of the working of the price mechanism to the international distribution of resources.

International trade can give rise to several different types of benefit. It can secure for a country goods, such as tropical fruits, which it is entirely unable to produce. It can make possible the realization of economies of large-scale production by extending the size of its market. It can provide a spur of competition for national monopolies (though this may be limited by the existence of giant multinational corporations). The advantages stressed most strongly in textbooks are those arising from the opportunities for international specialization and division of labour. Cost of production tend to vary from country to country as a result of differences in endowments of natural resources and supplies of accumulated man-made skills and capital equipment. The argument is usually expressed in a two-country two-commodity world, where it is clear that trade will be advantageous if one country enjoys absolutely lower real costs in one line and another in the second line of output. But it can be shown that trade can benefit both of two countries one of which has lower absolute costs of production in both commodities, provided only that the relative costs are different. The explanation of this phenomenon is known as the theory (or doctrine) of COMPARATIVE ADVANTAGE. This states that, where two countries have different relative (opportunity) costs of production, there will be a GAIN FROM TRADE, in the sense that it is possible for total world output of both goods to be increased if each specializes to a certain extent in the production of the good in which it has the greater advantage, or smaller disadvantage, in relative costs. It follows that a country with high production costs in all lines of output can nevertheless engage in trade with a low cost country to the benefit of both, as long as relative cost differences are not identical for all products. The division of any gain between countries depends upon the TERMS OF TRADE (the relationship between export prices and import prices). It should be added that potential gains must exceed transport costs for trade to be worthwhile.

The conclusions of the theory of comparative costs provide the basis of the economic case for FREE TRADE. The world, however, is one in which there are many impediments to trade. Most are the result of governmental restrictions imposed specifically in order to interfere with free trade. The most common are TARIFFS, or import duties, involving discriminatory taxes on imported goods. Others include export subsidies and import quotas whereby the volume (or value) of imported goods permitted is subject to a maximum limit. There are also non-tariff barriers (e.g. hidden subsidies resulting from the exemption of certain classes of domestic goods from taxes) which have grown in importance as tariffs have been lowered.

Some of the arguments for protection are fallacious, and deny the principle of comparative advantage. Notable among these is that to equalize costs of production in order to 'protect' a country from (the benefit it would derive from) trading with a country with lower costs. Some other arguments contain traces of validity, such as that for the protection of an infant industry, or to secure diversification for a country which is heavily dependent on a relatively small number of exports. Such arguments deny the relevance of current comparative advantage. They stress instead probable changes in relative advantage in the future (though it is not always made clear why profit-maximizing businessmen should not be as motivated by the promise of future as by present profits). Certain arguments for tariffs contain some strength, provided retaliatory action by other countries does not ensue. These include a tariff to cure domestic unemployment by restricting imports and a tariff aimed at reducing the price of imports (also known as 'making the foreigner pay' or 'improving the terms of trade'). The last of these is feasible only if a country holds the requisite monopoly power.

Most tariffs have objectives which are attainable by means other than by interfering with free trade. An example is a revenue tariff. Another is a tariff designed to ease the decline of a dying industry. A related argument concerns the distribution of income inside a country. While free trade may raise total world output, it need not increase everybody's real income. Indeed, international trade is a partial substitute for the international mobility of factors of production. It indirectly reduces a factor's scarcity by causing goods for which it is needed to be imported from countries where the factor is plentiful, thereby creating a tendency for the price of the factor made less scarce by trade to fall. Such an argument may also be related to questions of resource allocation. For instance, by protecting labour intensive industries real wages may tend to rise and an increase in the supply of labour be induced.

Finally, it should be noted that the case for free trade does not necessarily imply that a reduction of trade restrictions must involve only gains. Provided some restrictions remain, a partial reduction of tariffs may lead both to better resource allocation (called TRADE CREATION), and also to worse (TRADE DIVERSION). The latter can occur when parties to a CUSTOMS UNION lower tariffs between each other, buying, in consequence, from their trading partners some goods which are produced at lower cost in the rest of the world.

The financial aspects of international economics are best discussed in connection with the BALANCE OF PAYMENTS — the annual account of a nation's dealings with the rest of the world. It is usual to distinguish three sub-divisions of the balance of payments. The first deals with imports and exports of physical goods, the difference between the two being the surplus or deficit on the BALANCE OF TRADE. The second comprises trade in INVISIBLE services, like shipping, insurance, etc. The net position on visible and invisible trade together is referred to as the BALANCE ON CURRENT ACCOUNT. The third, CAPITAL ACCOUNT (also known as the INVESTMENT AND FINANCING ACCOUNT), lists all lending to and borrowing from non-residents. It is often sub-divided into two sections, one restricted to long-term and the other to short-term (or monetary) movements and residual transfers of gold and foreign currencies. The balance of payments on capital account is, by definition equal (but opposite in sign) to the balance on current account. Movements in international reserves apart, a deficit in the latter must mean that non-residents are making net loans to U.K. residents (albeit perhaps involuntarily) to allow an import surplus. Conversely, a surplus on current account means that the British are making net external loans. The idea that a balance of payments can be in deficit is, therefore, in a strict accounting sense a contradiction in terms.

While the balance of payments must formally balance, it is necessary to recognize a distinction between payments and receipts which arise for purely commercial reasons (AUTONOMOUS) and ACCOMMODATING payments, made usually by the State, e.g. in order to permit an import surplus, such as arranging a loan with a foreign government. These transactions are often hard to identify, but when commercially motivated payments and receipts are not equal, the balance of payments is generally said to be in DISEQUILIBRIUM. Frequently, the balance on current account is taken as a rough indication of the state of health of the balance of payments; though this can be misleading for a country which is importing capital for development, when a longer view is called for. The duration of investment is also important, e.g. a country which is borrowing on short term and lending long term may find itself in sudden difficulties. It is also useful to distinguish relatively stable direct investment (involving control of overseas companies) from the potentially more volatile portfolio acquisition of shares and other financial assets.

If the balance of payments is in disequilibrium, economic forces may, given time, tend towards a new equilibrium. The form that they take depends on institutional arrangements. Two extreme cases considered are those of FIXED and FLUCTUATING (or FLOATING) EXCHANGE RATES. The fixed exchange rate case is typified by the so-called GOLD STANDARD. Under this system governments guarantee to buy and sell gold at a fixed price in terms of their own currencies thereby fixing indirectly also the rate of exchange between them (apart from the costs of shipping gold). A deficit country losing gold may expect the equilibrating forces to take three forms. Assuming the money supply is reduced accordingly, (i) interest rates tend to rise attracting foreign capital, (ii) prices and wages tend to fall making exports more competitive, and (iii) incomes tend to fall leading to a decline in demand for imports. The extent to which movements in prices, incomes and interest rates help restore equilibrium depends on the elasticities of supply and demand for imports and exports and on MARGINAL PROPENSITIES TO IMPORT. The opposite influences may be felt by a creditor country. During the period between the two world wars a form of gold standard was in operation, but many creditor countries insulated their economies from the expansionary influence of gold inflows, thereby adding to the pressure on debtors.

The alternative to fixed exchange rates is to allow them to fluctuate with changes in the supply of and demand for foreign currency. A fall in the foreign demand for a country's exports tends to lower its exchange rate (and vice versa). This, in turn, tends to increase exports by making them cheaper to foreigners, to reduce imports by raising domestic prices and, therefore, to improve the balance of trade provided that the elasticities of demand for (and supply of) exports and imports are high enough. Exchange rate variations tend to work primarily through changes in relative prices, rather than through changes in income, and they may help provide some independence for a deficit country to adopt expansionist domestic policies, e.g. to promote growth and full employment. Fluctuating exchange rates are not, however, without disadvantages. Competitive lowering of exchange rates (DEVALUATION) by countries trying to 'export' their own unemployment may be self-defeating. Devaluation tends also to be inflationary and rising prices can wipe out temporary advantages. Moreover, speculative capital movements, induced by expectations of changes in the exchange rate, may be destabilizing (i.e. cause a movement away from equilibrium).

After the experience of competitive 'beggar-my-neighbour' devaluations in the 1930s, governments in many countries intervened in foreign exchange markets in order to try to insulate their currencies from fluctuations in supply and demand. At the end of the Second World War most western countries set up the International Monetary Fund (I.M.F.) to maintain a system of fixed exchange rates that could be altered only in special circumstances (ADJUSTABLE PEG). This did not preclude speculation. In fact devaluations under an adjustable peg system tend to be relatively large, if infrequent. The case for freeing exchange rates rests partly on a reduced incentive for speculation in so far as it means that the price of a currency can move continuously and in either direction — leaving speculators liable to losses as well as to gains. The I.M.F. rules were relaxed and sterling was freed to float in 1972.

A deficit country which does not resort to variations in the exchange rate as a remedy for balance of payments problems has three broad alternatives from which to choose. In the first place, it may obtain temporary relief by using up its reserves of gold and foreign currencies, and by obtaining loans from foreign banks, governments or international institutions. The larger the available cushion of international liquid assets the less need there is for other action. In the second place, a deficit country can put downward pressure on prices and incomes through a credit squeeze, price and wage control or similar policy. Finally, it may resort to restricting the demand for and supply of foreign exchange by introducing IMPORT CONTROLS (and export subsidies) on goods and EXCHANGE CONTROLS on capital transactions and other payments. Restrictions may be multilateral or discriminatory (i.e. directed against 'hard' currencies in the greatest excess demand).

During the depression of the 1930s world trade sank to a very low level. Most countries engaged in trade and exchange restrictions which tended to cancel each other out. Some groups of nations (such as the U.K. in the Sterling Area) made agreements to free trade and payments. A similar policy was pursued after the Second World War on a larger scale with the establishment of the International Monetary Fund, the International Bank for Reconstruction and Development and G.A.T.T. (the General Agreement on Tariffs and Trade). Closer ties grew up between some regional groupings, especially important for the U.K. being the Common Market (the European Economic Community), which Britain joined in 1973. By 1977 all import duties had been abolished on goods within the Market. British exchange controls were removed on all international payments in 1980.

ANALYSIS

Multiple Choice

Choose the alternative which provides the best answer to the question or completes the sentence most satisfactorily.

1 International trade is regarded as being distinct from interregional trade because

   (a) of the existence of different natural resources.
   (b) of the existence of different tastes.
   (c) of the existence of different natural abilities of labour.
   (d) factor mobilities differ between and with countries.
   (e) All of the above.

2 In its trade with the rest of the world a country will tend to specialize in the production of goods in which

   (a) its labour productivity is highest.
   (b) its costs of production are lowest.
   (c) it has the greatest comparative advantage or least comparative disadvantage.
   (d) it has either a comparative advantage or a comparative disadvantage.
   (e) world demand is greatest relative to supply.

3 There is unlikely to be a gain from international trade if

   (a) one country can produce some goods more efficiently but other goods less efficiently than other countries.
   (b) one country can produce all goods twice as efficiently as other countries.
   (c) the prices of all goods are strictly controlled in one country.
   (d) factors of production are completely immobile between countries.
   (e) all countries have precisely the same tastes.

4 Questions 4-8 are concerned with the theory of comparative advantage which applies in a world in which there are two countries, H and K, and two commodities, cheese and onions. Constant costs are assumed. Ignore costs of transport. With one unit of resources countries H and K can produce quantities of cheese or onions as stated in the tables. Select for each question which of the following is likely to follow from the theory.

   (a) H exports cheese and imports onions
   (b) K exports cheese and imports onions
   (c) H exports cheese and onions
   (d) K exports cheese and onions
   (e) No trade occurs

		Cheese	Onions
Country	H	10	10
	K	7	7

5

		Cheese	Onions
Country	H	6	4
	K	5	7

6

		Cheese	Onions
Country	H	12	8
	K	10	3

7

		Cheese	Onions
Country	H	4	12
	K	6	18

8

		Cheese	Onions
Country	H	4	2
	K	3	2

9

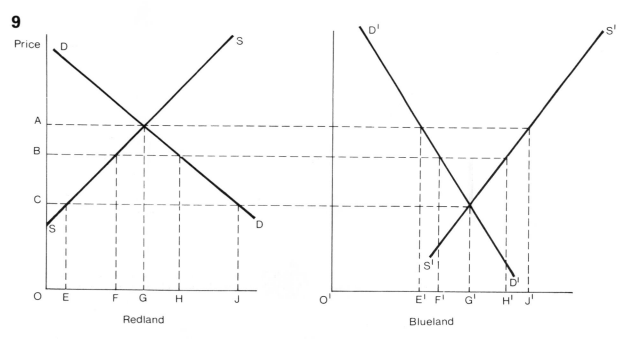

Fig. 7.1

The next two questions are based on Fig. 7.1 which portrays the domestic supply and demand curves for teapots in two countries, Redland and Blueland. They start to trade with each other.

The equilibrium world price and quantity traded are

(a) price OA; quantity OG.
(b) price OB; quantity FH.
(c) price OB; quantity OG.
(d) Price OC; quantity OJ.
(e) price OC; quantity EJ.

10 Which of the following statements correctly describes the quantity of teapots consumed in the importing country?

(a) Blueland consumes O'H'
(b) Blueland consumes O'G'
(c) Blueland consumes F'H'
(d) Redland consumes OH·
(e) Redland consumes OJ

11 If Hong Kong can produce everything twice as cheaply as Britain,

(a) trade will be advantageous to both countries if each concentrates on the production of goods in which it has a comparative advantage and Britain on those goods in which it has the smallest comparative disadvantage.
(b) trade will be advantageous to both countries if Hong Kong concentrates on the production of goods in which it has a comparative advantage and Britain on those goods in which it has the smallest comparative disadvantage.
(c) trade will be advantageous to Britain but not to Hong Kong.
(d) trade will be advantageous to Hong Kong but not to Britain.
(e) trade between the two countries will not be profitable.

12 Assume two countries A, with a plentiful supply of labour, and B, with a plentiful supply of land. Which of the following is likely to follow the opening up of trade between them?

(a) Rents will tend to fall relative to wages in A.
(b) Rents will tend to rise relative to wages in A and B.
(c) Rents will tend to fall relative to wages in B.
(d) Rents and wages will tend to rise in about the same proportions in A and B.
(e) None of the above.

13

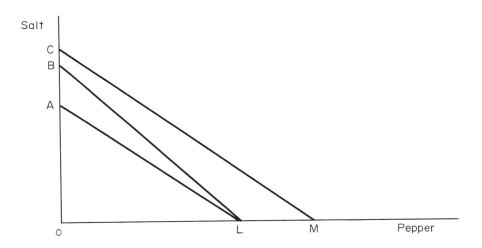

Fig. 7.2

Fig. 7.2 shows the production possibility curves of three countries, A, B and C, which are considering starting to trade with each other. If transport costs are zero, trade between

(a) A and B will lead to A importing pepper.
(b) A and C will lead to A exporting salt.
(c) B and C will lead to B importing salt.
(d) A and C will not take place because C has an absolute advantage in both salt and pepper.
(e) B and C will not take place because C can produce more salt and more pepper than B.

14 The terms of trade is the name given to the

(a)   conditions under which trade is carried on.
(b)   relationship between the price of imports and the price of exports.
(c)   proportion of a country's national income which is spent on imports.
(d)   difference between the value of exports and the value of imports.
(e)   measure of international differences in labour productivity.

15 Which of the following are valid economic objections to giving tariff protection to an infant industry?

1.   It is difficult to know in advance which industry merits it.
2.   There are too many new industries and one cannot afford to give protection to all of them.
3.   It may be hard to remove the tariff when it is no longer justified.
4.   Business men are as likely to be motivated by the prospect of adequate future profits as of immediate returns.
5.   A consumer subsidy on the product would be equally efficient.

(a)   1 and 2 only
(b)   2,3 and 5 only
(c)   1,3 and 4 only
(d)   1,3,4 and 5 only
(e)   1,2,3,4 and 5

16 Which of the following tend most to break the link between international prices?

(a)   Import duties
(b)   Import quotas
(c)   Export subsidies
(d)   Fixed exchange rates
(e)   Devaluation

17 The table below gives details of the domestic supply and demand schedules for footballs in the Republic of Ham.

Price ($)	Quantities supplied	Quantities demanded
2.00	200	650
2.50	300	600
3.00	400	550
3.50	500	500

The world market price of footballs is $2.50 and at this price Hamburgers can buy as many as they please. The government of Ham has imposed a duty of $0.50 on imports of footballs. How many footballs are imported in equilibrium?

(a)   150
(b)   500
(c)   550
(d)   600
(e)   650

18 Which of the following might be reasonably expected to follow the formation of a customs union by two countries in the world?

1.   The distribution of resources within the union will be less efficient.
2.   The distribution of resources between the union and the rest of the world will be more efficient.
3.   The world distribution of resources will be more efficient.
4.   The distribution of income within the customs union will be more just.
5.   The distribution of incomes inside the two countries joining the union will be more similar to each other.

(a)   2 only
(b)   5 only
(c)   1 and 4 only
(d)   2 and 3 only
(e)   3 and 5 only

19 The table below shows the quantities of francs supplied and demanded in the foreign exchange market at various rates of exchange with the pound sterling.

Price of sterling in francs	Francs demanded (m)	Francs supplied (m)
5	40	140
6	50	130
7	60	120
8	70	110
9	80	100
10	90	90
11	100	80

Which of the following conclusions can be drawn from the table.

1. The equilibrium exchange rate is 1 franc equals 10 pence.
2. If the British government wished to maintain an exchange rate of 11 francs to the pound, they should offer to sell 20 million francs in the market.
3. If the French government wished to maintain an exchange rate of 20 pence to the franc they should offer to buy 100 million francs in the market.
4. If the demand for francs rose by 25% at all exchange rates (supply remaining unchanged) the pound would buy one less franc in the market.
5. If the demand for francs rose by 25% at all exchange rates and the British government wished to prevent the rate of exchange from changing, they should offer to sell £22.5 million more francs in the market.

(1) 1 and 2 only
(b) 2,3 and 4 only
(c) 1,3 and 5 only
(d) 1,2,3 and 4 only
(e) 1,2,3,4 and 5

20

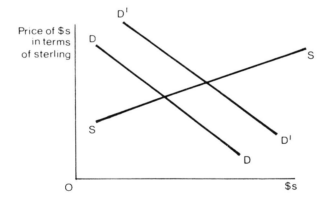

Fig. 7.3

Fig. 7.3 portrays the market for foreign exchange ($s). SS and DD are the supply and demand curves. Which of the following are likely to cause the demand curve to shift to D'D'?

1. A rise in the demand for British goods by foreigners
2. A rise in the demand for imports of foreign goods in the U.K.
3. A rise in the demand for British goods in the U.K.
4. A rise in interest rates abroad relative to those in the U.K.
5. A belief by foreigners that the value of sterling will fall
6. A belief by U.K. residents that the value of sterling will fall

(a) 1,2 and 3 only
(b) 2,4 and 6 only
(c) 2,4,5 and 6 only
(d) 1,3,4 and 5 only
(e) 1,2,3,4,5 and 6

21 Fixed exchange rates may be beneficial for a country because they

(a) lessen the likelihood that the balance of payments will become unfavourable.
(b) protect foreign exchange reserves.
(c) prevent speculation in the currency by non-residents.
(d) lessen the need for structural changes in the economy.
(e) reduce uncertainty for traders.

22 Country A, whose currency is dollars, imports cars from country B, whose currency is pounds. The exchange rate is $5 = £2 and the cars cost £5000 each. The exchange rate changes to £1 = $2. Which of the following is correct?

(a) Cars now rise in price by £2500.
(b) Cars now rise in price by $2500.
(c) Cars now fall in price by £2500.
(d) Cars now fall in price by $2500.
(e) The change in the exchange rate affects both the dollar and the pound price of cars.

23 Country A, whose currency is dollars, has a rate of inflation half that of country B, whose currency is pounds. If no government action is taken the probable effect will be to cause

(a) the real rate of interest in A to fall relative to B.
(b) the volume of A's imports to fall.
(c) the volume of A's exports to rise.
(d) the number of dollars obtainable for a pound to fall.
(e) private capital to move from B to A.

24 A country may offset an upward movement in its exchange rate by

(a) the sale of foreign currency by the central bank.
(b) the purchase of domestic currency by the central bank.
(c) the introduction of import controls.
(d) relaxing exchange controls.
(e) obtaining loans from other countries.

25 The following are the details of all international transactions except gold movements for three countries, I, II and III. Which of them is/are not in equilibrium on the balance of payments?

Country	Balance of		Net commercial capital movements Lending (−)/Borrowing (+)
	Visible trade	Invisible trade	
I	+25	−45	−30
II	− 5	− 5	+10
III	+ 5	+10	+15

(a) I only
(b) I and II
(c) I and III
(d) I, II and III
(e) None of them

26 From the viewpoint of the economy of Figmentia (F), which of the following should count as international liquid assets?

(a) F's borrowing rights with international agencies
(b) F's net credit on invisible trade
(c) F's credit balance on its current account in the balance of payments
(d) The current account deposits of F's residents with domestic banks
(e) Notes and coin in the vaults of F's central bank

27 Which of the following results in a credit in the invisible transactions section of the balance of payments?

(a) Inflows of capital
(b) Imports of goods
(c) Receipts of dividends by non-residents
(d) An increase in foreign exchange reserves
(e) Tourist visits by foreigners

28 Devaluation will tend to bring about a larger improvement in a country's balance of trade the

(a) less elastic the foreign demand for exports.
(b) less elastic the home demand for imports.
(c) more home prices rise after devaluation.
(d) greater the elasticities of demand for imports and exports.
(e) fewer substitutes there are for the exports of the devaluing country.

29 Last year Humbuggia exported $8000 and imported $9000 worth of goods and had a credit balance of $2500 worth of invisible trade items. Foreign lending was $2000 and borrowing from foreigners $3000. What happened to Humbuggia's foreign exchange reserves?

(a) They fell by $500
(b) They rose by $500
(c) They rose by $2500
(d) They fell by $3000
(e) They fell by $4500

30 The marginal propensity to import is

(a) total imports divided by national income.
(b) the relationship between a change in income and the consequent change in imports.
(c) national income divided by total imports.
(d) the relationship between a change in import prices and the consequent change in import quantities.
(e) the relationship between the price of imports and the price of exports.

31 Assume that a country begins to trade with the rest of the world and that the multiplier effect of a change in investment falls in consequence. The fall will tend to be greater

(a) the larger the total volume of imports.
(b) the smaller the total volume of exports.
(c) the greater the average propensity to import.
(d) the greater the marginal propensity to import.
(e) All of the above.

32 Which of the following are most likely to increase the rate of growth of output in a less developed country with a large population but little capital?

(a) Widespread use of birth control
(b) Employment of capital intensive techniques of production
(c) Employment of labour intensive techniques of production
(d) Reduced expenditure on education
(e) Redistributing income from rich to poor

Problems

1 The world consists of two countries, Rome and Athens. In Rome all available resources can produce 120 helmets or 24 swords. In Athens, all available resources can produce 60 helmets or 20 swords. Constant costs prevail in both countries.

(i)   In which good does Rome have a comparative advantage?
(ii)   In which good does Athens have a comparative disadvantage?
(iii) At what price would Rome find it advantageous to trade helmets for swords?
(iv)   At what price would Rome find it advantageous to trade swords for helmets?
(v)   At what price would Athens find it advantageous to trade helmets for swords?
(vi)   At what price would Athens find it advantageous to trade swords for helmets?

Each country in isolation devotes half its resources to producing (and consuming) each commodity.

(vii)   How many helmets and swords are produced by Rome?
(viii) How many helmets and swords are produced by Athens?

International trade opens up between the two countries at an exchange rate of 4 helmets for 1 sword. Athens produces only swords and exports 9 to Rome. Rome produces 100 helmets and devotes the rest of its resources to swords.

(ix)   How many helmets does Athens import from Rome?
(x)   How many swords does Rome produce for itself?
(xi)   What is total consumption of swords and helmets in Rome after trade?
(xii)   What is total consumption of swords and helmets in Athens after trade?
(xiii) What is the gain from trade for Rome?
(xiv)   What is the gain from trade for Athens?
(xv)   What is the total world gain from trade, in terms of helmets, at the ruling international exchange rate?

2 Fig. 7.4 portrays the market for furs in a country which trades with the rest of the world. The
curves marked SS and DD are the domestic supply and demand for furs. OA is the world price at
which any number of furs may be imported. AB is a tariff which the government imposes on the
import of furs.

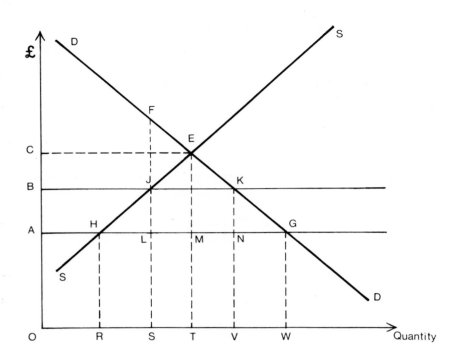

Fig. 7.4

Questions (i)-(v) refer to the situation before the tariff is imposed.

   (i)   What is the domestic price of furs?
  (ii)   What is the domestic consumption of furs?
 (iii)   What is the domestic production of furs?
  (iv)   How many furs are imported in equilibrium?
   (v)   How much is spent on imports in equilibrium?

Questions (vi)-(xi) refer to the situation after the imposition of the tariff.

  (vi)   By how much does the domestic price of furs change?
 (vii)   By how much does the domestic consumption of furs change?
(viii)   By how much does the domestic production of furs change?
  (ix)   By how much does the volume of imports change?
   (x)   By how much does the amount of sterling received by foreigners change?
  (xi)   What is the government revenue from the tariff?

Instead of a tariff the government decides to use import quotas to protect domestic industry.
Licenses are issued giving the right to buy OS furs.

 (xii)   What is the domestic free market price of furs?
(xiii)   At what price would exporters offer OS furs to licence holders?
 (xiv)   What is the maximum sum importers would be prepared to pay for all the licences to import
       furs?

3 The following information is known about the international finances of Blueland.

	£m
Loans made to foreigners	100
Exports of goods	245
Interest and dividends earned abroad by Bluelanders	15
Other invisible receipts	65
Repayment by foreigners of a loan made 5 years ago	10
Total gold reserves	500
Imports of goods by Bluelanders	250
Net long-term overseas financial assets owned by Bluelanders	75
Interest and dividends paid to foreigners	20
Other invisible payments	30
Loans received from foreigners	50
Gold inflow/outflow	?

(i) Calculate its net gold movement and construct its balance of payments in the space provided.

Current Account   £m

Capital Account

(ii) What is the balance of trade?
(iii) What is the balance on current account?
(iv) Assume that all current account transactions and borrowing by Bluelanders is made on normal commercial principles, and half lending by Blueland consists of government loans. What is Blueland's net surplus or deficit?

4 The curves DD and SS in Fig. 7.5 represent the demand and supply curves for francs by British and
French in a market where the exchange rate is free to fluctuate.

    (i)   The equilibrium exchange rate is how many pence per franc?
   (ii)   The equilibrium exchange rate is how many francs per penny?
 (iii)   How many francs are bought in equilibrium?
  (iv)   How many pence are sold in equilibrium?

The following circumstances must now be taken into account. Select from the curves in the diagram
those which correspond best to each market situation described. Each question is a separate one
and each change should be related to the original situation described above.

    (v)   The British demand for French goods rises. By how much does the exchange rate alter?
  (vi)   The French demand for British goods rises. What is the equilibrium exchange rate?
 (vii)   The rate of interest rises in France. How many francs are sold in equilibrium?
(viii)   The exchange rate is expected to move against the penny. What is the most likely
           equilibrium exchange rate?
  (ix)   The exchange rate is expected to move against the franc. What is the most likely
           equilibrium exchange rate?
   (x)   The original conditions hold, but the French government decides to fix the exchange rate
           at OE by buying or selling francs in the market as necessary to maintain it. What action
           will they need to take?

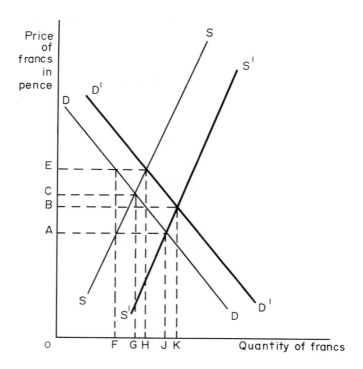

Fig. 7.5

5 The inhabitants of Mythica produce almonds and bricks in isolation from the rest of the world, and are faced by a production possibility curve CE and indifference curves as shown in Fig. 7.6. It comes to their notice that the price of bricks in terms of almonds in the world market is given by the slope of the line CG, and the possibility of benefiting from trade is suggested to them.

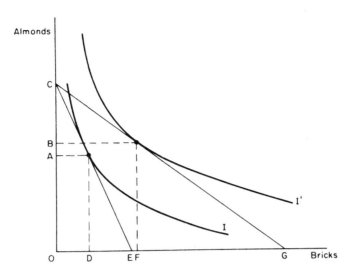

Fig. 7.6

(i)   What are the maximum quantities of (a) almonds and (b) bricks that Mythica could produce in isolation?
(ii)   What are the maximum quantities of (a) almonds and (b) bricks that Mythica could obtain by trading with the rest of the world?
(iii) How many bricks are produced and consumed in isolation?
(iv)   How many almonds are produced and consumed in isolation?
(v)   Which commodity will be exported?
(vi)   How much will be exported?
(vii) How much will be imported?
(viii) What is the gain from trade?

U.K. ECONOMY

Multiple Choice

Choose the alternative which provides the best answer to the question or completes the sentence most satisfactorily.

1 Which of the following countries has the (i) largest and (ii) smallest share of world exports of manufactured goods?

(a) France
(b) Japan
(c) U.K.
(d) U.S.A.
(e) W. Germany

2 Which of the following countries spends the highest proportion of its income on imports?

(a) France
(b) Japan
(c) Belgium
(d) U.K.
(e) U.S.A.

3 The proportion of its income which the U.K. spends on imports is approximately

    (a) 5%
    (b) 10%
    (c) 25%
    (d) 40%
    (e) 60%

4 Which of the following groups of countries provides (i) the largest market for U.K. exports and (ii) the largest source of U.K. imports?

    (a) North America
    (b) European Economic Community
    (c) Rest of Europe including U.S.S.R.
    (d) Oil exporting countries
    (e) Japan

5 Which of the following categories of U.K. (i) imports and (ii) exports is most important in value terms?

    (a) Foodstuffs
    (b) Crude materials
    (c) Fuel
    (d) Chemicals
    (e) Manufactures

6 For which of the following foodstuffs does the U.K. rely least on imports?

    (a) Cheese
    (b) Butter
    (c) Eggs
    (d) Sugar
    (e) Wheat

7 Which of the following invisible trade items usually show the most favourable net balance for the U.K.?

    (a) Private sector interest, profits and dividends
    (b) Government receipts and payments
    (c) Travel
    (d) Shipping
    (e) None of the above. All are equally favourable.

8 Which of the following have been generally most (i) favourable and (ii) unfavourable to the U.K. in the years since 1960.

    (a) The balance of visible trade
    (b) The balance of invisible trade
    (c) The balance on current account
    (d) The balance on capital account
    (e) The balance on current and capital accounts

9 The balance of payments of the U.K. was relatively strong in the early 1980s. A major cause of this was probably

    (a) the abolition of exchange controls in 1980.
    (b) the relatively low interest rates in the U.K.
    (c) North Sea oil.
    (d) the high rate of economic growth in Britain.
    (e) All of the above.

10 Approximately how many months' imports could be purchased with the U.K.'s official gold and foreign currency reserves?

    (a) 3 months
    (b) 12 months
    (c) 2 years
    (d) 3 years
    (e) 5 years

11 Which of the following statements about the total value of British overseas assets around 1980 is correct?

(a) They accounted for approximately half the national wealth.
(b) They were roughly equal to overseas liabilities.
(c) They would have bought about three years' normal imports.
(d) They were worth about half of their value ten years earlier.
(e) They would have covered the deficit on the current account of the balance of payments in all except the worst year in the 1970s.

12 All but one of the following are, in general, permitted by G.A.T.T. Which is the exception?

(a) Export subsidies
(b) Import duties
(c) Devaluation
(d) Floating exchange rates
(e) Tariff reductions

13 Which of the following led to an improvement in international liquidity?

(a) The fall in the world price of gold
(b) Increased lending by the I.B.R.D.
(c) The rise in interest rates throughout most countries in the world
(d) The introduction of S.D.R.s
(e) All of the above

14 All but THREE of the following countries are members of the European Economic Community. Which are the exceptions?

I. Austria	VII. Italy
II. Belgium	VIII. Netherlands
III. Denmark	IX. Norway
IV. France	X. Sweden
V. Greece	XI. United Kingdom
VI. Ireland	

(a) I, IX and X
(b) II, III and VIII
(c) IV, V and VI
(d) V, IX and XI
(e) VI, VII and X

15 Which of the following is a multinational corporation?

(a) International Monetary Fund
(b) International Finance Corporation
(c) International Tin Council
(d) General Motors
(e) All of the above

16 Which of the following are concerned with the economic development of Third World countries?

(a) I.B.R.D.
(b) I.D.A.
(c) I.F.C.
(d) U.N.C.T.A.D.
(e) All of the above

17 Which of the following organizations is primarily concerned with (i) tariff reductions and (ii) the price of oil?

(a) G.A.T.T.
(b) I.B.R.D.
(c) I.L.O.
(d) I.M.F.
(e) O.P.E.C.

18 Five countries are listed below in order of their real income per capita in the late 1970s. Only one ordering is correct. Which is it?

(a) Sweden	(b) Canada	(c) Japan	(d) U.S.A.	(e) France
Finland	U.K.	W. Germany	Switzerland	Spain
Israel	Australia	U.K.	U.K.	U.K.
U.K.	Pakistan	Mexico	Ireland	Greece
Cyprus	Italy	Uganda	India	Burma

Exercises

Note: Sources are suggested for all exercises. Altneratives may be available if the one mentioned is not in your library. For advice on them and on the collection and presentation of data in tabular and graphical form see pp ix–x.

1 Calculate the percentage increase in the value of the U.K.'s imports and exports of each of the following commodity groups over the last 5 or 10 years.

	Exports £m		Imports £m		Percentage increase 19.... to 19....	
	19....	19....	19....	19....	Exports	Imports
Food, beverages and tobacco						
Crude materials						
Fuels						
Chemicals						
Manufactured goods						
Machinery and equipment						
Other						

Source: Annual Abstract of Statistics

   (i)   Which groups increased most and least over the period?
  (ii)   To what extent can you attribute any changes in your answer to (i) above to the E.E.C.?
 (iii)   How similar or different from that before the Second World War is the commodity composition of the U.K.'s import and export trade?

2 Prepare four bar charts showing the relative importance of the following groups of countries in U.K. import and export trade for a recent year and for another 5 or 10 years previously (Source: Annual Abstract of Statistics):

        E.E.C.
        Rest of Western Europe
        North America
        South Africa, Japan, Australia and New Zealand
        Oil exporting countries
        Other 'developing countries'
        Centrally planned economies

   (i)   Which groups have increased in relative importance between the two years on (a) the import and (b) the export side? Can you offer explanations for such changes as you have noted?
  (ii)   Where are the largest markets today for U.K. exports? Are any of them the same as in the pre-Second World War period?

3 Collect figures of the index numbers of the 'unit value' (a rough measure of price) and the volume of U.K. imports and exports for the last 10 years. (Source: Annual Abstract of Statistics.) Prepare two scatter diagrams on graph paper, one to show the relationship between price and volume (quantity) for imports and the other for exports. Plot a point on each diagram for every year and label it with the date. How strong do you perceive the correlation between price and quantity to be for (a) imports and (b) exports. Would you expect the correlations to be positive or negative? Why? Can you tell from the figures whether the demand for imports and exports is elastic or inelastic?

4 Prepare two graphs each showing three series over the last 10 years. On one graph plot the volume of U.K. imports, the terms of trade and Gross Domestic Product. On the other graph plot the volume of U.K. exports, the terms of trade and some index of economic activity in the rest of the world (e.g. GNP in the U.S.A., world industrial production or O.E.C.D. industrial production). Do the indexes of economic activity or the terms of trade appear to be the better associated with U.K. imports and exports? (A good source for data for this question is the National Institute Economic Review.)

5 Find from the Annual Abstract of Statistics the value of U.K. imports and exports of road vehicles last year and 10 years ago. Was this country a net importer or exporter in either year? In so far as there was any change in the net position between the two dates would you be inclined to attribute it to differences in prices, qualities, advertising or other factors associated with British and foreign cars and lorries? (Reference to a recent edition of Motoring Which? published by the Consumers' Association might help you answer this question.)

6 The various components parts of the balance of payments can easily change significantly from one year to another. In the space provided below calculate for each of the items listed the average value for the balance of payments on current account for the last 3 years.

	19....	19....	19....	Average 3 years		19....	19....	19....	Average 3 years £m
Exports					Imports				
Balance of visible trade									
Invisible receipts: Government(general)					Invisible payments				
Transport									
Travel									
Interest, etc.									
Transfers									
Other									
Total invisibles									
Balance of invisible trade									
Balance on current account									

Source: Annual Abstract of Statistics

(i) Did the U.K. have a deficit or a surplus on visible and invisible trade and on the balance on current account in any of the years and on an average of all three?

(ii) What are the chief ways in which a deficit on the current account may be financed?

7 Find out, from the Annual Abstract of Statistics, in how many of the last 10 years the U.K. was a net investor (rather than borrower) overseas on private account, i.e. ignoring governmental transactions. Why do British persons and institutions lend to others in foreign countries? How can such investment be financed? What difference does it make (a) to the balance of payments and (b) to the vulnerability of sterling whether such investment is short-term or long-term?

8 Extract from the National Institute Economic Review index numbers of consumer prices in the U.K. and the U.S.A. for the last 10 years. Divide the former by the latter to yield an index which gives some idea of the extent to which British prices have risen relative to those in America. (If the index has a value greater than 1 inflation has been relatively more rapid in this country and vice versa.) Plot the series on graph paper.

Now obtain figures of the sterling-dollar rate of exchange over the same period. Take the average number of dollars exchangeable for a pound in each year or the rate on 31 December, whichever is easier to ascertain (Source: Annual Abstract of Statistics or The Times business section). Turn the rate of exchange into an index number by dividing the rate in each year by that in the first year of your ten (and multiplying by 100 to put it in percentage terms.) The index for the first year will then be 100. Plot this series also on the graph. Are the two series correlated? Would you expect them to be? Why or why not?

9 For each of the countries in the table below find out how much the index of consumer prices has risen and how much the value of exports has increased (or decreased) over the last two years. Have the counties with the highest rates of inflation tended to have the largest or the smallest rises in export values? Would you have expected the results you found? If so, why? If not, how can you account for the disparity?

	Percentage change 19.... to 19....	
	Consumer prices	Value of exports
France		
Germany		
Italy		
Japan		
U.S.A.		
U.K.		

Source: National Institute Economic Review

Essays

1. Why do some countries produce for themselves goods that they could have imported more cheaply?

2. Are there any reasons for distinguishing between trade between England and Wales, on the one hand, and between England and France on the other?

3. What is the relationship between the notion of opportunity cost and the theory of comparative advantage?

4. How far is it true to say that the source of any gain from trade lies in the different endowments of factors of production possessed by different countries?

5. Explain the fact that although American productivity is much higher than Yugoslavia's, it may still pay both countries to trade. Would it still be true if Yugoslav productivity was exactly half American in all lines of output?

6. What are the terms of trade. What do they depend on? What are the implications of changes in the terms of trade for a country?

7. If free trade between Germany and Japan merely results in the Japanese driving Volkswagens and the Germans driving Datsuns, can this be described by any stretch of the imagination as a 'gain'?

8. 'Arguments for tariffs would all be much stronger if one could rule out the possibility of retaliation by other countries.' Discuss.

9. Why do economists seem, in general, to prefer tariffs to import quotas?

10. Evaluate the case for giving tariff protection to the British motor industry.

11. Why should countries wish to join a customs union with other countries? Should they expect any disadvantages to follow?

12. On what kind of goods would a government choose to impose a tariff if its sole purpose was to raise the maximum revenue? Would it make any difference if it also wanted the main burden to fall on foreigners?

13. How far is the state of a country's balance of payments a good indicator of its economic prosperity?

14. Explain the criteria for allocating international transactions to the visible trade, invisible trade or capital accounts of the balance of payments.

15. Why is it said that a country in surplus on its balance of payments is just as much in disequilibrium as a country in deficit? Is it under the same pressure to do something about it?

16. What alternatives are open to a country which is faced with a balance of payments problem?

17. Does inflation necessarily lead to a downward movement in a country's exchange rate?

18. Why is it argued that speculation is less under floating than under fixed exchange rates? On what assumptions is the argument based?

19. Explain why the effectiveness of a devaluation in so far as it concerns a country's balance of trade is dependent upon the elasticities of demand for imports and exports. Does it depend upon anything else?

20. Describe the relationships between imports and the national income and exports and the national income. Is there any sense in which exports could be likened to investment expenditure?

21. What is the purpose of foreign exchange reserves?

22. Why does the U.K. sometimes seek loans from international agencies?

23. How far do you consider that aid is a satisfactory alternative to protection for a developing country?

24. How different and similar are the benefits derived by the U.K. from membership of the E.E.C. and of G.A.T.T.?

CHAPTER 8

Economic Policy

(This chapter is concerned with questions of economic policy and employs analysis treated earlier in the book. Some major issues are brought together here, but the reader should refer back to previous chapters for fuller treatment of particular matters and for additional questions and problems.)

The activities of government are not confined to economic matters though the State has certain functions which are essentially economic. The scope of government intervention has increased enormously during the present century in the U.K. economy, as elsewhere, as most western countries have changed from being predominantly free-market to become more mixed-type economies.

The economic functions of the modern State may be described in conjunction with the objectives of economic policy. Several goals, or targets, can be distinguished — economic growth, full employment, stability of the price level, efficient allocation of resources and an equitable distribution of income and wealth. Other goals may be implied by these (e.g. raising productivity); they may be specific to a particular country (e.g. population control); or they may secondary goals in the sense that they are necessary for the achievement of primary goals (e.g. the balance of payments). The setting of goals is a political matter and the economist's role is to give advice on policies likely to achieve them efficiently.

It is not uncommon for economists to differ on questions of economic policy. Political views apart, the reasons may be found in disagreements about how the economy works and on the effects of alternative policies. Moreover, it is no easy political task to set national objectives, several of which may not be mutually consistent. A policy may be successful with respect to one goal at the expense of moving away from another. A policy for growth, for instance, may threaten the balance of payments or distributive goals, and a conflict between price stability and full employment may also be experienced. The economist can best advise on the most efficient policy to achieve a given set of goals if they are ranked in order of importance and expressed in precise quantitative terms.

There are several ways of classifying the economic functions of government, but a simple division between macroeconomic concern with the level of national output, employment and price stability, and microeconomic concern with the allocation of resources is a useful first approximation.

Some attention was given to the macroeconomic role of government in previous chapters, which stressed the role of aggregate demand and supply in determining the level of national income and of prices. There are three principal ways in which the State can intervene in the economy to try to promote economic growth, full employment and price stability. They are fiscal, monetary and prices-incomes policies, and it should be repeated that the choice between them is a matter of great controversy among economists.

Fiscal policy can affect aggregate demand either directly by changing the levels of total government revenue and expenditure (budgeting for a surplus or deficit as required, or changing the Public Sector Borrowing Requirement, PSBR) or indirectly by altering the tax structure to stimulate private sector consumption or investment expenditure. Taxes can be either automatic stabilizers (which change automatically as income changes, e.g. progressive income taxes) or discretionary (which require positive acts by ministers to initiate them). Monetary policy affects aggregate demand by means of changes in the quantity of money and/or interest rates. Prices-incomes policies involve the setting of guide-lines for wage and price increases aimed principally at the control of inflation.

No attempt can be made here to describe all the complexities of the debate, largely between Keynesians and Monetarists, on the advantages and disadvantages of different policy instruments. The background to the controversy is an imperfect understanding of the precise way in which the economy functions, the time lags involved, and the presence or absence of a faith in the efficiency of market forces themselves. Monetarists, sceptical of interventionist governments, tend to stress the difficulties involved with discretionary policies and to favour reliance on an automatic formula for increasing the money supply annually by an amount corresponding to the average growth of output. Keynesians tend to be sceptical of the efficiency of market forces in the short run and to advocate a policy mix of fiscal and monetary instruments (with perhaps a place for prices and incomes policies) to reduce cyclical fluctuations.

The debate is thought by some to hinge, too, on whether the control of inflation or full employment and economic growth are the prime policy targets. The advantages of the last of these are obvious. Price stability is desirable mainly because of the distributive effects of inflation, though

though these can be lessened by indexation, and because inflation tends to encourage investment of a 'hedging' kind (e.g. in 'collectables') rather than in real productive enterprise. It must be added that the balance of payments can act as a constraint on domestic macroeconomic policies and that flexible, rather than fixed, exchange rates tend to be favoured as offering greater independence for a nation to carry out its preferred programme.

Turning to the question of government intervention in the functioning of the price mechanism, it is useful to recall first the manner in which market prices act as signals equating supply and demand for different products. In perfectly competitive markets, a case can be made that the allocation of resources through the price mechanism is efficient. If one accepts that the amount individuals pay for a good is an adequate measure of society's satisfaction from it, then this proposition follows from the fact that, under perfect competition, the benefit accruing from the last unit produced is equal to the cost of producing it (marginal cost = price = marginal utility). Where, on the other hand, markets are imperfect it can be shown that resource allocation may not be efficient. A monopolist may not need to use the lowest cost combinations of inputs, and a profit-maximizing monopolist restricts output to the level where marginal cost is equal to marginal revenue (and less than price). Imperfect information about market conditions may also impede the efficient allocation of resources. Consumers, for example, may not be able to choose sensibly between competing products because they are unable to assess their different qualities. And individuals may not be able to decide whether to undergo training to acquire particular skills because they do not know what the demand for their services will be when they have finished training.

In addition to divergencies from perfect competition, there are two special kinds of goods where market price acts as an inadequate signal of consumer wants. The first are called PUBLIC (or COLLECTIVE CONSUMPTION) goods, such as national defence or the police force, which are consumed collectively by the community as a whole. Characteristically, a public good is one where the marginal cost of supplying it to additional consumers is zero. (There is no less street lighting to guide you at night, for example, if I walk along as well.) The second kind of goods are those with what are called EXTERNAL (SPILL-OVER or NEIGHBOURHOOD) EFFECTS, where for instance the benefit deriving from a commodity or service is not confined to persons consuming it but 'spills over' to others, e.g. a vaccination, which reduces the chance of passing a disease on as well as that of contracting it oneself. The example just given is one where SOCIAL BENEFITS are said to exceed PRIVATE BENEFITS. The converse case is illustrated by pollution or by a radio played on a crowded beach. These two instances involve externalities in consumption. Where there are external economies (or diseconomies) in production, changes in output by one firm lower (or raise) costs in another firm. SOCIAL COSTS here are said to differ from PRIVATE COSTS.

Two further cases must be mentioned where governmental interference with the free working of the price mechanism may be considered justified. The first is where the state takes a PATERNALISTIC attitude because of the belief that people would otherwise buy either less or more of certain products than is 'really' good for them (or for their children), e.g. health and education, on the one hand; drugs and pornographic literature on the other. In the second place, dissatisfaction may be felt with the allocation of resources in a free market because of the existing DISTRIBUTION OF INCOME, which affects the distribution of 'votes' that individuals have in the market place. Inequalities in income arise from market imperfections, but also from 'chance' factors such as inherited wealth, place of birth, sex, ability, age, etc. It is usual for a nation to want to alter its income distribution in what it believes is a more equitable direction (which does not necessarily mean a more equal one).

There are many ways in which a government may intervene in the market place, though the choice depends upon the particular circumstance it wishes to try and influence. There are, in principle, two methods available. The first tries to make the market work better by means of taxes, subsidies, price controls and regulations. The second consists of the replacement of the market by State ownership. All the main causes of 'market failure' lend themselves to alternative treatments. If the distribution of income is regarded as unsatisfactory, for example, the State can tackle the problem, inter alia, through changes in taxes, through the system of social services or by entering the factor market to influence the process of wage determination. To take one other example, the presence of monopolies can be approached in several ways, e.g. by transferring them to public ownership, by removing barriers to entry to increase competition or by deploying taxes and subsidies in order to affect profit-maximizing output. It is worth recalling that in the case of natural monopolies due to economies of scale, breaking up the monopoly may be inefficient. In the U.K. legislation passed since the end of the Second World War included the appointment of a Monopolies and Mergers Commission, a Restrictive Practices Court and an Office of Fair Trading.

Nationalization, or any form of public ownership, even if politically acceptable, does not in itself mean that the problems of an industry are at an end. Price and output policy must still be decided, and the criterion of profit maximization is rarely appropriate for a monopolist, even for one in public hands. Setting output at a level where price is equal to marginal cost may be a useful guide, though it can, at the same time, involve an industry in losses, where full costs are not covered. There may also be a case for running an industry at a loss because of the nature of the product (i.e. one with external economies).

Where the tax system is used to improve the distribution of resources or of incomes, the prime necessity is to establish carefully the precise objective which is being sought. The tax chosen should be that which best achieves its particular goal, while having the least undesirable side-effects on others (including macroeconomic goals). Conflict between the equity and incentive effects of taxes is particularly common, and it is necessary to try to establish the incidence of a tax, i.e. the persons on whom the burden of paying it truly falls. Finally, a tax should also be judged by reference to the costs of collection borne by the Exchequer and the taxpayer.

The U.K. has a wide range of different taxes. They are often classified into two categories: (1) taxes on incomes (sometimes called 'direct' taxes), e.g. income and profits taxes, and (2) taxes on expenditure (sometimes called 'indirect' taxes), e.g. V.A.T. and petrol tax. But there are some taxes, like those on the transfer of property (C.T.T.), which do not fit easily into either class. In analyzing the effects of a tax it is important to consider both the <u>average</u> rate of tax paid, which particularly affects income distribution, and the <u>marginal</u> tax rate, <u>which</u> is relevant to the substitution effects of taxation. Where the average rate of tax does not vary with income, the tax is called PROPORTIONATE, to distinguish it from PROGRESSIVE (and REGRESSIVE) taxes, where the proportion rises (with progressive taxes) or falls (with regressive taxes) as income rises. LUMP SUM (or <u>poll</u>) taxes have no substitution effects because the marginal tax rate is zero and they, therefore, have <u>minimal</u> effects on resource allocation.

Government expenditure covers the main purposes described in earlier paragraphs. The chief distinction to be drawn on this side is between <u>expenditure on goods and services</u> (for defence, education, roads, etc.) and <u>transfer payments</u> (e.g. pensions and unemployment benefits). Only the former constitute a real 'drain' by the public sector on the national output (and they are sometimes called <u>exhaustive</u> expenditures to distinguish them from transfers). Certain activities, of which education is by far the most important, are left in the hands of local authorities, which levy RATES on the value of property in their areas.

Three economic problems face a government with regard to its expenditure: (1) which goods should be produced, (2) how many of each of them and (3) how their costs should be covered. The first two are often approached through what is known as cost-benefit analysis. Such studies attempt to enumerate and evaluate all the direct and indirect benefits which are expected to accrue to the community as a result of a particular item of public expenditure, such as a motorway. The monetary value of indirect benefits is not always easily arrived at without making rather arbitrary assumptions, e.g. of the value to be placed upon human life. But the technique has been increasingly used in recent years to try to provide a means of assessing and comparing alternative programmes of public expenditure.

The final problem is how to cover the costs of government-provided goods and services. There are, in principle, only two alternatives. They may be supplied free (as with schools) or priced so that users are charged for them. The real costs have to be borne by someone. Whether the general taxpayer or the user should be responsible is largely a political matter.

ANALYSIS

Multiple Choice

Choose the alternative which provides the best answer to the question or completes the sentence most satisfactorily.

In this chapter, which involves matters of economic policy, it is sometimes difficult to keep value judgements entirely separate. In questions which discuss the efficiency of the pricing system you should assume, in general, that the market mechanism works well except in so far as specific defects are mentioned in a particular question. Remember that there may be more than one conceivable answer to the question. You are asked to choose <u>the best</u>.

1 Which of the following reasons is most likely to explain why two economists might disagree, <u>as economists</u>, on economic policy?

    (a) They have different views of the likely effects of a particular policy.
    (b) They are not agreed about which policy goals should be aimed at.
    (c) They disagree about the relative importance of alternative policy goals.
    (d) They are likely to be affected differently as individuals by alternative policies.
    (e) They differ in their views of the extent to which an economic theory can be put to the test.

2 The macroeconomic objective accepted as being of (i) prime and (ii) least importance is

    (a) the control of inflation.
    (b) full employment.
    (c) a high rate of economic growth.
    (d) an efficient allocation of resources.
    (e) not necessarily any of the above.

3 From the following list of national economic objectives choose the two pairs which are least likely to conflict.

    1. Full employment and balance of payments surplus
    2. Full employment and price stability
    3. Full employment and economic growth
    4. Price stability and balance of payments surplus
    5. Economic growth and price stability

    (a) 1 and 2 only
    (b) 1 and 3 only
    (c) 2 and 5 only
    (d) 3 and 4 only
    (e) 4 and 5 only

4 A tax is known as a built-in or automatic stabilizer if the

    (a) yield of the tax is automatically kept constant.
    (b) rate of tax changes automatically as the price level changes.
    (c) total revenue from the tax varies inversely with income.
    (d) yield of the tax varies positively with income.
    (e) tax is automatically brought forward for consideration when stabilization problems arise.

5 Which of the following policy instruments have their <u>primary</u> impact through (i) fiscal and (ii) prices-incomes policies, rather than through monetary policy?

    (a) Changes in the tax rates
    (b) Price controls
    (c) Changes in interest rates
    (d) Open-market operations
    (e) Calls for Special Deposits

6 The difference between monetary policy (MP) and fiscal policy (FP) is that

    (a) MP is automatic, FP is discretionary.
    (b) MP concerns the money supply, FP the rate of interest.
    (c) FP involves changes in taxation, MP government expenditure.
    (d) FP tries to control aggregate demand through budgetary means, MP through the quantity of money and the rate of interest.
    (e) Not necessarily any of the above.

7 Which of the following are generally considered to be disadvantages of using prices-incomes policies to try to control inflation?

    1. They interfere with the allocation of resources.
    2. They tend to cause unemployment to rise.
    3. They are unfair as some incomes are virtually uncontrollable.
    4. They interfere with free collective bargaining.
    5. They distort skill differentials.
    6. They reduce the effectiveness of monetary policy.
    7. They adversely affect the balance of payments.

    (a) 1,2 and 4 only
    (b) 1,4 and 5 only
    (c) 3,5 and 6 only
    (d) 2,3,6 and 7 only
    (e) 1,2,3,4,5,6 and 7

8 Which of the following would make fiscal policy more likely to succeed in preventing a depression?

    1. Resources are efficiently allocated.
    2. Private spending varies inversely with government spending.
    3. Discretionary tax changes are speedily effected.
    4. The balance of payments is not adversely affected.
    5. Private investment expenditure can be accurately predicted.

    (a) 1,2 and 3 only
    (b) 1,3 and 5 only
    (c) 1,2,4 and 5 only
    (d) 2,4 and 5 only
    (e) 3,4 and 5 only

9 Choose from the following the circumstances most likely to lead to accelerating inflation.

    (a) Trade unions bargain over real rather than money wages.
    (b) The supply of money is held down by government policy.
    (c) The community's expectations of the future level of prices are continuously revised downwards.
    (d) The economy is below rather than above full employment output.
    (e) The rate of interest is rising rather than falling.

10 A country finds that it has a deficit on its current account on the balance of payments. Which of the following policies may help to protect its foreign exchange reserves?

1. Devaluation
2. Deflation
3. Import controls
4. Export subsidies
5. Exchange controls
6. Raising the rate of interest

(a) 1 and 2 only
(b) 3 and 4 only
(c) 2,3,4 and 6 only
(d) 1,2,5 and 6 only
(e) 1,2,3,4,5 and 6

11 A country is operating under a system of fixed exchange rates. Choose from the following objectives that which is most likely to be the most difficult to achieve because of the influence of the balance of payments.

(a) Reducing the rate of inflation
(b) Redistributing income
(c) Raising the rate of economic growth
(d) Reducing the degree of monopoly power
(e) Increasing the mobility of labour

12 A customs union is formed between two countries, Deliria (D) and Whimsica (W). Which of the following results is likely?

1. Both D and W will find it easier to adopt expansionist monetary and fiscal policies.
2. Both D and W will be in better positions to control their exchange rates.
3. D will be better able to protect its industries from competition from W, and vice versa.
4. Resource allocation between D and W will improve.
5. There will be more scope for the exploitation of comparative advantages between D-W and the rest of the world.

(a) 4 only
(b) 4 and 5 only
(c) 1 and 2 only
(d) 1,2,4 and 5 only
(e) 1,2,3,4 and 5

13 In order for the free working of the price mechanism to be generally recognized to work well it is necessary that

(a) consumers' voting power should accurately reflect income distribution.
(b) income distribution should be equal.
(c) incomes should accurately reflect individuals' contributions to national output.
(d) incomes should not be affected by inheritance.
(e) income distribution should be regarded as equitable.

14 If the distribution of income is regarded as being unfair the price mechanism may for this reason fail to allocate resources satisfactorily, ceteris paribus, because

(a) marginal utilities are not equal to prices for all goods.
(b) marginal costs are not equal to prices for all goods.
(c) factor prices are not equal to marginal productivities.
(d) some goods may have spill-over effects.
(e) a fairer distribution might lead to a better allocation of resources.

15 A market is operating efficiently except only that inadequate information is available about two television sets, one of which is more reliable than the other. The price mechanism will not work perfectly because

(a) expected marginal utility will equal price but not realized utility.
(b) expected utility will equal realized utility but not price.
(c) television sets are, by the definition implied in the question, public goods.
(d) the effect on income distribution will be unsatisfactory.
(e) All of the above

16 Which of the following may be used to justify State intervention in the provision of health services?

(a) The fact that some services have beneficial spin-offs.
(b) Imperfect knowledge of the benefits that different health services may bring.
(c) The distribution of income is unfair.
(d) Some beneficiaries (e.g. children) do not themselves make health expenditure decisions.
(e) All of the above

17 If as a result of income redistribution the top 10% of income receivers have a smaller proportion of total income

(a) income distribution must be more equal.
(b) the top 10% of income receivers must have lower living standards.
(c) the lowest 10% of income receivers must be relatively better off.
(d) the lowest 90% of income receivers must be relatively better off.
(e) All of the above

18 Public goods are those which

(a) are bought by members of the public as distinct from the government.
(b) if one individual consumes more of them this does not necessitate reduced consumption by other individuals.
(c) people buy without realizing that they will not get satisfaction from them.
(d) are produced by a public company as distinct from a nationalized industry.
(e) private firms will not supply because of the existence of taxation.

19 If a market is operating efficiently except that there are external economies in the consumption of harps and external diseconomies in the production of rattles, the free market will tend to result in

(a) too many harps and too many rattles.
(b) too many harps and too few rattles.
(c) too many rattles and too few harps.
(d) too few rattles and too few harps.
(e) the right amount of harps and rattles.

20 When I have a telephone installed other people can ring me. When I am making a call they cannot. Externalities are therefore involved which imply certain of the following:

1. telephone installations should be taxed.
2. telephone installations should be subsidized.
3. telephone charges for calls should be taxed.
4. telephone charges for calls should be subsidized.

(a) 1 only
(b) 1 and 3 only
(c) 1 and 4 only
(d) 2 and 3 only
(e) 2 and 4 only

21 A publicly owned marina cost £10 000 to construct when the rate of interest was 10%. The rate of interest is now 20% and 500 persons want to use the marina once each per annum. No maintenance or any other costs are incurred. What is the most efficient economic price to charge?

(a) Zero
(b) £2
(c) £4
(d) £20
(e) £24

22 Firm A pollutes a river affecting firm B downstream. The 'optimum' amount of pollution is

(a) zero.
(b) where the marginal cost to the government of removing the pollution is zero.
(c) where the marginal cost to the government of removing the pollution exceeds the marginal benefit of it to A.
(d) where the marginal cost of the pollution to B equals its marginal benefit to A.
(e) where the marginal cost of the pollution to A equals its marginal benefit to B.

23 Which of the following could act as an incentive for a profit-maximizing monopolist to produce the same output as would be forthcoming under perfect competition?

(a) The imposition of a tax on output
(b) Price control
(c) An increase of the tax on monopoly profits
(d) A reduction of the tax on monopoly profits
(e) The granting of a patent

24 A State monopoly with falling average costs of production faces a downward-sloping demand curve. Under which of the following conditions would it be making losses?

(a) It produces an output where marginal cost is less than marginal revenue.
(b) It produces an output where average cost is less than average revenue.
(c) It produces an output where marginal cost is equal to price.
(d) It produces an output where marginal revenue is zero.
(e) Its total variable costs exceed its total fixed costs.

25 A profit-maximizing monopolist is suddenly subjected to a 50% tax on its profits. This will normally lead it to

(a) raise the price of its product.
(b) reduce its inputs of factors of production.
(c) lower its output.
(d) both lower its output and raise the price of its product.
(e) leave its price, output and inputs of factors of production unchanged.

26 Fig. 8.1 shows the supply and demand curves for a commodity under different alternative demand conditions represented by D^1 and D^2. The government imposes a unit tax equal to the vertical distance between S and S+t. Which of the following conclusions can be drawn from the diagram?

(a) The price to the consumer rises less with D^1 because it is less elastic.
(b) The price received by the producer falls less with D^2 because it is more elastic.
(c) The quantity sold falls more with D^2 because it is less elastic.
(d) Total government revenue is greater with D^2 because it is less elastic.
(e) The government revenue per unit is less with D^1 because it is more elastic.

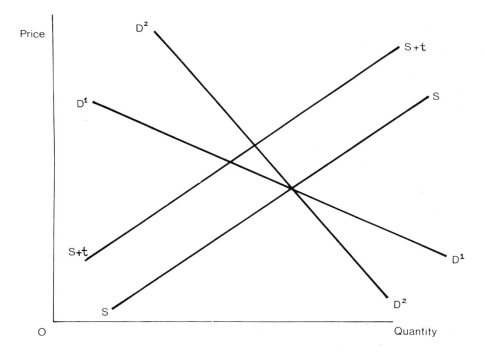

Fig. 8.1

27 An argument often used against using taxation to reduce the inequality of income is that

  (a) the marginal utility of income falls as income rises.
  (b) the rate of economic growth may suffer.
  (c) savings may be overstimulated.
  (d) immigration may be encouraged.
  (e) it would be widely regarded as inequitable.

28 The marginal tax rate is greater than the average tax rate for a

  (a) poll tax.
  (b) proportionate tax.
  (c) progressive tax.
  (d) regressive tax.
  (e) lump sum tax.

29 A regressive tax will tend to

  (a) redistribute income more equitably.
  (b) redistribute income more inequitably.
  (c) redistribute income more unequally.
  (d) redistribute income more equally.
  (e) not redistribute income unless the tax proceeds are redistributed.

30 The table below shows the market supply and demand schedules for melons. The government decides to impose a tax of 10 pence per unit of quantity sold. What changes occur in the equilbrium market price and quantity of melons?

Price (pence)	Quantity supplied	Quantity demanded
15	150	250
16	160	240
17	170	230
18	180	220
19	190	210
20	200	200
21	210	190
22	220	180
23	230	170
24	240	160
25	250	150

  (a) Price rises by 5 pence and quantity falls by 100.
  (b) Price rises by 5 pence and quantity falls by 50.
  (c) Price rises by 10 pence and quantity falls by 100.
  (d) Price falls by 10 pence and quantity rises by 50.
  (e) Price falls by 10 pence and quantity rises by 100.

31 Which of the following interferes least with the allocation of resources in a market which is otherwise accepted as ideal?

  (a) A poll tax
  (b) A progressive income tax
  (c) An excise tax
  (d) A regressive tax
  (e) Any kind of subsidy

32 A capital gains tax is one which is levied on

  (a) the value of stock market securities owned by an individual.
  (b) the value of the capital assets owned by a business.
  (c) asset sales at prices in excess of their purchase prices.
  (d) capital transfers, such as gifts.
  (e) capital movements in the balance of payments.

33 If the government introduces a progressive income tax in addition to its existing taxes, this will tend to

(a) increase the amount of leisure taken.
(b) increase the amount of work done.
(c) increase the amount of work done only if the income effect of the tax is greater than the substitution effect.
(d) increase the amount of work done only if the income effect of the tax is less than the substitution effect.
(e) have an adverse effect on incentives to work and to take leisure, provided the tax has no substitution effect.

Problems

1 In each of the diagram I to VI (Fig. 8.2) an original supply curve (SS) is shifted as a result of government policy. Which diagram or diagrams correspond to the policy changes described below?

(i) A specific tax per unit
(ii) A specific subsidy per unit
(iii) An 'ad valorem' tax
(iv) An 'ad valorem' subsidy
(v) A progressive income tax

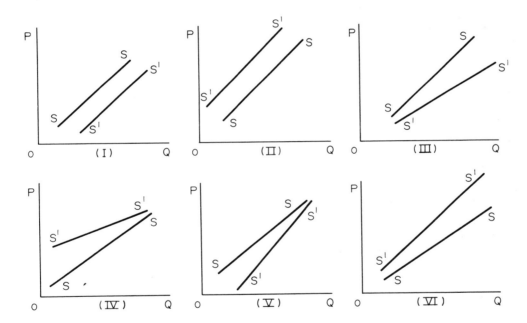

Fig. 8.2

2 The supply and demand schedules for the commodity used in problem 2, Chapter 2, are repeated below:

Price (pence)	Weekly quantities	
	Demanded	Supplied
12	0	440
11	0	400
10	60	360
9	120	320
8	180	280
7	240	240
6	300	200
5	360	160
4	420	120
3	480	80
2	540	40
1	600	0

The government decides to place a tax of 5p per unit on suppliers of the commodity.

  (i)   How many will be supplied at the old equilibrium price of 7p?
 (ii)   What is the excess demand at the price of 7p?
(iii)   What is the equilibrium quantity supplied after tax?
 (iv)   How much does the tax raise price to the consumer?
  (v)   How much does the tax lower price to the producer?
 (vi)   What is the government revenue from the tax?
(vii)   If the demand schedule and equilibrium price were as given, but supply had been perfectly inelastic, what would the post-tax equilibrium price have been?
(viii)   If conditions of (vii) above had held, what would government revenue have been?
 (ix)   If conditions of (vii) above had held, how much would the tax have lowered price to the producer?

3 The government is considering improving road conditions between L and M. The alternative projects being considered are as follows:

  A.   Improve the existing road. Cost per annum: £50 million
  B.   Build an additional single-track road. Cost per annum: £150 million
  C.   Build an additional double-track road. Cost per annum: £450 million
  D.   Build an additional motorway. Cost per annum: £1300 million

The annual benefit accruing from the new roads is estimated at £100, £300, £600 and £1400 million for alternatives A, B, C and D respectively.

  (i)   Which project should be undertaken?
 (ii)   The matter is further considered, and it is realized that the calculated benefits ignore the saving in time of traffic using the old road, which is now less congested. The total hours saved per annum are estimated as 50, 100 and 200 million on projects B, C and D respectively. The value of time is estimated at £1.00 per hour. Which project should be undertaken?
(iii)   What additional or more reasonable assumptions can you suggest to improve the cost-benefit estimates?

4 Winkworth Golf Club in the centre of the city of Chestminster has lodged a planning application to buy twenty hectares of adjacent public parkland. S. Hambles Ltd, a local building company, has put in a counter-application to purchase the same land to build a residential housing estate. You are an economic adviser for the minister responsible for deciding whether to accede to either request. Submit a report in outline identifying the major economic issues involved.

5 Which of the tax schedules in Fig. 8.3 correspond to

   (i)   proportional taxation?
   (ii) progressive taxation?
   (iii) regressive taxation?
   (iv) the most steeply progressive taxation?
   (v)   the most steeply regressive taxation?

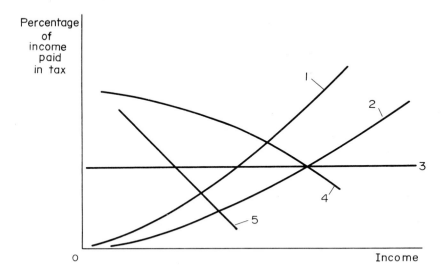

Fig. 8.3

6 Bob Scarlett is able to work any number of hours overtime from 1 to 4 at a rate of £1.25 per hour on top of his normal day. He puts a figure of £15 on the total value of his leisure when he does not work overtime, and £14.25, £13.25, £12.00 and £10.50 when he works 1, 2, 3 and 4 hours respectively.

   (i)   How many hours overtime does he work?
   (ii) The government puts a flat rate 20% tax on overtime earnings. How many hours does he work?
   (iii) The government puts a progressive income tax on overtime earnings, 20% on the first hour, 40% on the second hour and 60% on 3 or more hours. How many hours does he work?
   (iv) The government puts a tax of 75p on him if he works any overtime at all. How many does he work?
   (v)   Reconsider the flat rate 20% income tax in (ii) above. But now take account of the fact that Bob puts quite a different value on his leisure time. Working overtime increases his income and allows him to enjoy his leisure more at first, but he easily gets bored with too much of it. The actual valuation he puts on his total leisure when he does not work any overtime is £15. When he works one hour overtime the value he puts on his remaining leisure is £14.25 and the values for 2, 3 and 4 hours overtime are £14.25, £14.75 and £15.75 respectively. How many hours overtime would he work?

7

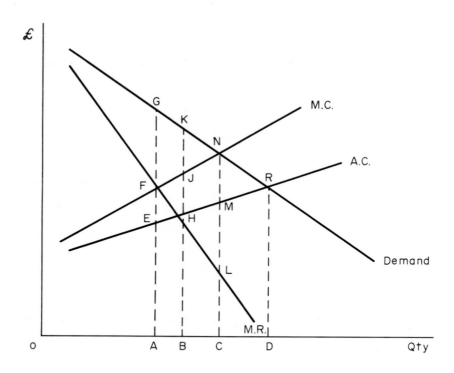

Fig. 8.4

A profit-maximizing monopolist is faced with the cost and demand conditions in Fig. 8.4.
M.C. = marginal cost, A.C. = average cost and M.R. = marginal revenue.

- (i) What is monopoly output?
- (ii) At what price is the output in (i) sold?
- (iii) What are monopoly profits in (i) and (ii)?
- (iv) What would be the output under perfect competition?
- (v) What legally imposed maximum price would induce the monopolist to produce the output in (iv)?
- (vi) What would be the monopoly profits in (v)?
- (vii) What tax would induce the monopolist to produce perfectly competitive output?
- (viii) What subsidy per unit of output would induce the monopolist to produce perfectly competitive output?
- (ix) What would be monopoly profits including subsidy in (viii)?

8   Workland does not trade at all with the outside world. Investment expenditure is always a constant £300. Consumption expenditure is always three-quarters of disposable income. (Treat each question as independent unless otherwise stated.)

- (i) What is the equilibrium level of income?
- (ii) The government decides to build a new school costing £100, out of past savings, so does not need to levy any taxes. What is the equilibrium level of income?
- (iii) Full employment income is £1400. How much must the government raise or lower its expenditure to ensure that the equilibrium level is exactly equal to the full employment level?
- (iv) Full employment income is £900. How much must the government raise or lower its expenditure to ensure that the equilibrium level is exactly equal to the full employment level?
- (v) The government decides to levy a $33\frac{1}{3}$% income tax without spending it. What is the equilibrium level of income?
- (vi) The government levies the tax in (v) above, and also spends £450 on a new road. What is the equilibrium level of income?
- (vii) What is the size of the government's budget surplus or deficit in (vi) above?

U.K. ECONOMY

Multiple Choice

Choose the alternative which provides the best answer to the question or completes the sentence most satisfactorily.

1 Which of the following nationalized industries is the largest employer?

(a) British Electricity
(b) British Gas
(c) British Rail
(d) British Steel
(e) The Post Office

2 What proportion of the national income is the total revenue of the central and local government in Britain?

(a) 25%
(b) 35%
(c) 50%
(d) 65%
(e) 75%

3 What proportion of total expenditure on goods and services is made by the central and local government in Britain?

(a) 15%
(b) 30%
(c) 45%
(d) 60%
(e) 75%

4 For which of the following countries is the total tax burden (i) the highest and (ii) the lowest percentage of GNP?

(a) Japan
(b) Sweden
(c) U.K.
(d) U.S.A.
(e) W. Germany

5 The share of public expenditure on the social services as a proportion of national income since the beginning of the present century has

(a) remained roughly constant.
(b) more than doubled.
(c) fallen slightly.
(d) fallen substantially.
(e) risen in money terms but fallen in real terms.

6 Which of the following describes most accurately the finance of local government current expenditure in Britain in recent years?

(a) The main finance comes from the central government.
(b) The main finance comes from rates.
(c) The main finance comes from sources other than rates and from the central government.
(d) The main finance comes from council house rents.
(e) Rates and grants from the central government supply over three-quarters of total revenue.

7 Which of the following is the largest expenditure item of local authorities in the U.K.?

(a) Education
(b) Health
(c) Police and justice
(d) Housing
(e) Interest on debt

8 Which of the following is the largest item of central government expenditure in the U.K.?

(a) Education
(b) Roads
(c) Agriculture
(d) Defence
(e) National Debt interest payments

9 Which of the following British taxes has the largest total yield?

(a) Corporation tax
(b) Value added tax
(c) Capital gains tax
(d) Personal income tax
(e) Taxes on alcohol and tobacco

10 The proportion of taxpayers who are liable to tax at rates no higher than the basic tax rate in the U.K. is approximately

(a) 40%.
(b) 55%.
(c) 65%.
(d) 80%.
(e) 95%.

11 The marginal tax rate on earned income for persons in the highest tax bracket in the unified personal tax system introduced in 1980 was

(a) $82\frac{1}{2}$%.
(b) 75%.
(c) 60%.
(d) 55%.
(e) 30%.

(Note: Find out also at what level of taxable income the top rate was paid.)

12 The Investment Income Surcharge is a tax on

(a) personal incomes received as dividends and interest.
(b) personal incomes in the highest tax brackets.
(c) company incomes ploughed back rather than distributed to shareholders.
(d) capital gains resulting from the sale of investments.
(e) the income of investment trusts before distribution to shareholders.

13 Under V.A.T. in the U.K. a business is normally charged tax on its sales to its customers. Choose from the following list of circumstances those which allow exemption from such tax.

1. The goods are exported.
2. The business is a service industry rather than one supplying goods.
3. The sales are of educational goods and services.
4. The business has an annual turnover which is less than a stipulated small amount.
5. The sales are of foodstuffs.
6. The business is a nationalized industry.

(a) 1,2,3 and 4
(b) 1,2,5 and 6
(c) 1,3,4 and 5
(d) 2,4 and 6 only
(e) 3,5 and 6 only

14 Which of the following policies have been adopted by the government to try and bring down the rate of inflation?

1. Placing cash limits on public expenditure
2. Raising the P.S.B.R
3. Sales of securities by the Bank of England
4. Seeking agreement with the trade unions on wage rate increases
5. Setting targets for sterling M3

(a) 5 only
(b) 2 and 3 only
(c) 1,3 and 4 only
(d) 1,4 and 5 only
(e) 1,2,3,4 and 5

15 Which of the following have been used by the British Government to influence the location of industry?

    (a)   Industrial development certificates
    (b)   Loans
    (c)   Grants
    (d)   Supply of services
    (e)   All the above

16 Which of the following is the government-sponsored body which has been most concerned with promoting economic growth?

    (a)   N.E.D.O.
    (b)   C.B.I.
    (c)   Committee of Public Accounts
    (d)   Department of Employment
    (e)   A.C.A.S.

17 With one exception all the following are official bodies concerned with the settlement of industrial disputes between trade unions and management. Which is the exception?

    (a)   Joint Industrial Councils
    (b)   A.C.A.S.
    (c)   Committees of Enquiry
    (d)   Central Arbitration Committee
    (e)   Industrial Tribunals

18 Which of the following are government bodies whose major concern is with competition policy?

    1.   City Take-over Panel
    2.   Confederation of British Industry
    3.   Monopolies and Mergers Commission
    4.   National Economic Development Council
    5.   Office of Fair Trading
    6.   Restrictive Practices Court

    (a)   3 only
    (b)   3 and 4 only
    (c)   3,5 and 6 only
    (d)   1,3,5,6 and 7 only
    (e)   1,2,3,4,5,6 and 7

19 Which of the following statements about competition policy in Britain is correct?

    (a)   Less than 5% of mergers referred to the Monopolies and Mergers Commission have been found to be against the public interest.
    (b)   Less than 5% of referrable mergers have been referred to the Monopolies and Mergers Commission.
    (c)   Less than 5% of cases brought before the Restrictive Practices Court have been found to be against the public interest.
    (d)   Monopolies controlling more than 25% of a market must be broken up unless they can satisfy the Monopolies and Mergers Commission that they are not acting against the public interest.
    (e)   The Office of Fair Trading was created in 1973 to take over the role of the Restrictive Practices Court set up in 1956.

20 All but one of the following are 'gateways' through which an agreement may be allowed by the Restrictive Practices Court. Which is the exception?

    (a)   The agreement prevents serious unemployment.
    (b)   The agreement is necessary as protection against other restrictive practices.
    (c)   The agreement benefits exports.
    (d)   The agreement protects the public against injury.
    (e)   The agreement provides a benefit to the public which outweighs any damage done by it.

Exercises

Note: Sources are suggested for all exercises. Alternatives may be available if the one mentioned is not in your library. For advice on them and on the collection and presentation of data in tabular and graphical form see pp ix-x

1 There are many ways of measuring the importance of government in the British economy. Use the Annual Abstract of Statistics to calculate the following for a recent year:

> Central government total tax receipts as a percentage of GDP
> Central government total expenditure as a percentage of national income
> General government final consumprion as a percentage of total consumer expenditure
> Gross domestic fixed capital formation of a public corporations, central government and local authorities as a percentage of total gross fixed capital formation by all sectors
> Total employment in public administration and defence as a percentage of total employment

  (i)   What is the range between the largest and smallest percentages you found? Which, if any, do you regard as the most relevant and why?

 (ii)   Suggest three different measures of the importance of government in the economy (and find estimates of them if you can).

(iii)   What is the point of trying to measure the importance of government economic activity? (Be careful! There is more than one point.)

2 Complete the following table showing the main items of central government revenue for last year and for 10 years ago. Calculate each as a percentage of the total.

	19....		19....	
	£m	%	£m	%
Taxes on income				
Taxes on expenditure				
National Insurance, etc. contributions				
Other sources				
TOTAL REVENUE		100%		100%

Source: Annual Abstract of Statistics

  (i)   Give two examples of each of the following: taxes on income, taxes on expenditure and other sources of revenue.

 (ii)   Which of the categories in the table are the most progressive?

(iii)   Have there been any major changes in sources of revenue between the two dates? Would you wish there to have been in order to improve the efficiency or equity of the economy?

3 From the table analyzing general government expenditure in the Annual Abstract of Statistics run down the list of items and use your judgment to decide as best you can for each of them whether more or less than half expenditure by the State is of an exhaustive type or consists of transfers. Allocate the items into two groups according to this criterion. Tot up the total expenditure of the two groups and calculate the percentages that each bears to the total. Repeat the exercise for a year 5 or 10 years previously. Have the percentages changed? If so can you explain what this means and why it has occurred? For which of the two groups would you recommend an increase in relative importance in order to make the economy (a) more efficient and (b) fairer?

4 Refer to a press report of the last Budget speech by the Chancellor of the Exchequer.

  (i)   What new taxes did he introduce, if any, and why?

 (ii)   What taxes did he abolish, if any, and why?

(iii)   What taxes did he raise, if any, and why?

 (iv)   What taxes did he lower, if any, and why?

  (v)   What plans did he have for the Public Sector Borrowing Requirement?

 (vi)   Estimate the effect in general terms of any of the changes in tax upon (a) the allocation of resources, (b) the distribution of income, (c) the supply of saving, (d) the level of national income, (e) the general level of prices, (f) the cost of tax collection and (g) tax evasion and avoidance.

5 Complete the following table with figures of the main items of the revenue and expenditure of local authorities for a recent year. Calculate each as a percentage of the total.

	£m	%
Revenue		
Central government		
grants		
loans		
Rates		
Other sources of income		
TOTAL		
Expenditure		
Education		
Housing		
Environmental services and roads		
Interest on debt		
Other expenditure		
TOTAL		100%

Source: Annual Abstract of Statistics

(i) Give an example of 'other income' and 'other expenditure'.

(ii) How are 'rates' calculated?

(iii) Which of the major expenditure categories are mainly exhaustive or transfer expenditures?

(iv) Are there any significant ways in which the income and/or expenditure patterns differ from those of the central government?

6 Collect information to complete the following table showing the numbers of incomes subject to tax in each size class shown for the most recent year available.

Range of pre-tax income	Pre-tax				Post-tax			
	Numbers of incomes		Total income		Numbers of incomes		Total income	
	Nos	%	£m	%	Nos	%	£m	%
	(a)	(b)	(c)	(d)	(e)	(f)	(g)	(h)
Under £2000								
£2000 to £4999								
£5000 to £9999								
£10 000 to £49 999								
£50 000 and over								
All incomes		100%		100%		100%		100%

Source: Annual Abstract of Statistics

(i) Calculate the percentages of the totals in columns (b), (d), (f) and (h). How do the shares of total income of the relatively rich and poor differ before and after tax?

(ii) How much tax did each group pay? What are their average tax rates? What additional information would help you calculate their marginal tax rates?

(iii) How wealthy would you need to be to get into the top income bracket if your entire income was in the form of dividends on ordinary shares? (Use the average dividend yield on ordinary shares in the Annual Abstract of Statistics for your calculation.)

(iv) Why should you not accept the difference between pre- and post-tax income alone as measuring the redistributive effect of government policy?

7 (i) Choose a busy main road junction with traffic lights in your district. Assume it would cost £50 000 to build a pedestrian bridge over it. Assume also that it would last 10 years, have zero maintenance costs and zero scrap value at the end. How much benefit would it need to yield to be worth building? Make a short survey to estimate roughly how much total time saving there would be per annum to motorists and to pedestrians at not having to stop when the lights were against them. At what price per hour would the time saved make the bridge worth building?

(Ignore discounting problems, i.e. assume all benefits and costs have the same money value at the present time regardless of when they occur.)

(ii) Suppose that the building of the bridge would also save the lives of, on average, four children a year, each of whom would otherwise have been expected to have earned £10 000 per annum during his or her working life. What differences would be made to the net benefits estimated in (i) above if you took account of the saving of lives? How satisfactory do you consider it to be to take lost earning power as an estimate of the value of a human life? Can you think of a better way of valuing it?

8 Using the index to The Times or The Economist find references to two reports of the Monopolies and Mergers Commission. One of these should be on a single firm monopoly and the other on a merger. To what extent did the Commission find that (i) monopoly power existed or would be increased by the proposed merger and (ii) the firm or firms were earning 'excessive' profits? How would such profits be possible? If no excessive profits were earned does this mean that the firm(s) were necessarily operating efficiently?

9 Obtain copies of recent annual reports of any pair of nationalized industries (e.g. National Coal Board and British Railways Board). Compare their profit/loss records. Do you think that either or both deserve government subsidies on economic grounds? Why or why not? Try to find out how much they did receive by way of subsidy last year.

10 Using data from the Monthly Digest of Statistics, prepare a graph showing, for the last 12 months, the following series:

> Money stock, sterling M1
> Average rate of interest on Treasury bills
> Public Sector Borrowing Requirement

Can the graph provide any clues at all as to whether the government was engaged on an expansionary or contractionary macroeconomic policy and whether it was relying on fiscal, monetary or other policy instruments? What additional information might help you reach a conclusion on these matters? What do you think was the prime objective that the government was trying to pursue in its economic policy in the last 12 months?

11 Using data from the Annual Abstract of Statistics, prepare a graph showing, for the last 5 years, the following series:

> Current account surplus/deficit on the balance of payments
> Official reserves (of gold, foreign currencies and I.M.F. drawing rights)
> Sterling price of dollars

Can you tell from the graph whether the balance of payments acted as a constraint on domestic economic policy during the period? What additional information would help you decide if it did? What means could the government have used to try and correct a disequilibrium on the balance of payments?

Essays

1. What are the 'goals' of British economic policy? How consistent are they with each other?

2. Why do economists sometimes support different economic policies?

3. How desirable is a high rate of economic growth?

4. How much justification is there in preferring the control of inflation to the prevention of unemployment as the prime objective of economic policy.

5. What is meant by inflation? What causes it to accelerate?

6. Explain the difference between fiscal and monetary policy.

7. 'The Keynesian-Monetarist controversy is the major issue of macroeconomic policy of the age.' What is the controversy about?

8. 'Prices and incomes policies spell the death of the free-market economy.' Discuss.

9. What economic policy objectives might be achieved by lowering import duties?

10. How far does the state of the balance of payments inhibit domestic economic policy?

11. Has time shown that the benefits of membership of the E.E.C. have outweighed the costs?

12. Why is it important that the distribution of income should be regarded as fair if a market system is to allocate resources satisfactorily?

13. What criteria should be used by the government in deciding whether an industry should receive a subsidy?

14. 'The most effective policy for the control of monopoly lies in the removal of barriers to entry.' Discuss with illustrations.

15. Compare the effectiveness for the control of monopoly of policies (a) setting a maximum price for its product and (b) forcing it to charge a price equal to its marginal cost of production.

16. Why does the government adopt a location of industry policy?

17. Can a case be made out for the nationalization of an industry because it is making losses?

18. How can taxes and subsidies be used to improve the allocation of resources?

19. Consider the implications of replacing £10 million of revenue from income tax by a tax on Sunday motoring.

20. How far do you agree that the tax on beer is regressive and a disincentive to effort?

21. Is V.A.T. a better tax than income tax in any respects?

22. Taxes can be redistributive. Can government expenditures be so too?

23. How different are the arguments that the State should build the nation's roads and that it should make decisions on how much should be spent on them?

24. Is it inconsistent to argue that the government should spend more on health services in Britain and that the charges for treatment should be raised?

25. Is there any economic justification for letting people into public parks free but charging for facilities like tennis and boating inside them?

26. Compare the reasons why governments interfere in the market for (a) education and agriculture or (b) opera and house rents.

27. How would you set about deciding how much the State should spend on (a) refuse disposal and (b) public libraries?

28. Show, with examples, how the price mechanism can be used as a policy instrument for the allocation of resources in the case of (a) pollution, (b) monopoly and (c) housing.

29. Should all forms of pollution be banned on economic grounds?

Answers

Chapter 1 The Subject Matter of Economics

ANALYSIS

Multiple Choice

1.	(e)	4.	(d)	7.	(c)	10.	(e)	13.	(b)	16.	(d)
2.	(a)	5.	(c)	8.	(d)	11.	(e)	14.	(a)	17.	(c)
3.	(b)	6.	(a)	9.	(d)	12.	(c)	15.	(a)		

Problems

1. (i) 2
   (ii) 3
   (iii) 2
   (iv) AA'
   (v) AA'
   (vi) 1

2. (i) Increase
   (ii) Increase
   (iii) Decrease
   (iv) 9 bananas
   (v) (a) Constant
       (b) 7 bananas

3. (i) A, B and C
   (ii) E
   (iii) E
   (iv) D
   (v) E

U.K. ECONOMY

Multiple Choice

1. (e)
2. (i)(e), (ii)(b), (iii)(d), (iv)(c)
3. (b)
4. (i)(a), (ii)(d)
5. (i)(a), (ii)(d)
6. (i)(d), (ii)(a)

7. (c)
8. (i)(b), (ii)(c)
9. (i)(c), (ii)(d)
10. (i)(e), (ii)(b)
11. (i)(a), (ii)(e)
12. (b)

Chapter 2 Supply and Demand

ANALYSIS

Multiple Choice

1.	(d)	8.	(d)	15.	(b)	22.	(d)	29.	(e)	36.	(c)
2.	(c)	9.	(i)(b), (ii)(c)	16.	(d)	23.	(e)	30.	(e)	37.	(b)
3.	(a)	10.	(c)	17.	(e)	24.	(c)	31.	(d)	38.	(e)
4.	(e)	11.	(c)	18.	(b)	25.	(b)	32.	(a)	39.	(d)
5.	(a)	12.	(a)	19.	(b)	26.	(e)	33.	(b)	40.	(b)
6.	(d)	13.	(c)	20.	(a)	27.	(i)(c), (ii)(d)	34.	(c)	41.	(c)
7.	(a)	14.	(a)	21.	(e)	28.	(b)	35.	(e)	42.	(b)

Problems

1. (i) OP_2
   (ii) OQ_2
   (iii) OP_1
   (iv) OP_3
   (v) (a) Zero, (b) Q_1Q_3
   (vi) (a) $-Q_1Q_3$, (b) Zero

2. (ii) 7p and 240
   (iii) 6p and 200
   (iv) 6p and 300
   (v) 10p and 260
   (vi) 5p
   (vii) Excess supply of 120

149

3. (i) 2 and S
    (ii) D and 4
    (iii) 1 and S
    (iv) D and 3
    (v) 2 and S
    (vi) 1 and S
    (vii) 1 and 4
    (viii) D and 4
    (ix) 1 and S
    (x) 1 and 4

4. (i) 4
    (ii) $1\frac{1}{2}$
    (iii) 1
    (iv) 100
    (v) 5250

5. (i) H and F
    (ii) A and B
    (iii) G and E
    (iv) A
    (v) D
    (vi) The same
    (vii) (−)1
    (viii) (−)$\frac{1}{2}$
    (ix) (−)2

6. (i) A
    (ii) B and E
    (iii) None
    (iv) C
    (v) A and D
    (vi) F

7. (i) I
    (ii) IV
    (iii) I and III
    (iv) None
    (v) V
    (vi) I, III and IV
    (vii) IV
    (viii) I and IV
    (ix) You cannot tell
    (x) I
    (xi) None
    (xii) V
    (xiii) I and IV
    (xiv) II

8. (iii) £4.50
   (iv) 5 pots
   (v) 30p
   (vi) £4.50
   (vii) Bob's
   (viii) Bob's
   (ix) 50p

9. (ii) 9
   (iii) 9
   (iv) 25
   (v) 12p
   (vi) 10p
   (vii) 9 oranges, 5 bananas
   (viii) 28
   (ix) 7 oranges, 14 bananas
   (x) Income effect: 4 bananas
       Substitution effect: 5 bananas (approx.)

10. (i) OB
     (ii) OH
     (iii) AF
     (iv) $\frac{OA}{OB}$
     (v) HK
     (vi) OE
     (vii) Cannot tell
     (viii) Income effect: JK
            Substitution effect: HJ
     (ix) Income consumption curve: M and R
          Price consumption curve: L and R
     (x) AG

Chapter 3   Production: Costs and Organization

ANALYSIS

Multiple Choice

1. (b)
2. (e)
3. (i)(a), (ii)(d)
4. (c)
5. (c)
6. (e)
7. (d)
8. (b)
9. (a)
10. (c)
11. (b)
12. (d)
13. (d)
14. (i)(e), (ii)(a)
15. (a)
16. (i)(a), (ii)(b)
17. (a)
18. (c)
19. (c)
20. (c)
21. (d)
22. (c)
23. (b)
24. (d)
25. (e)
26. (a)
27. (e)
28. (a)
29. (d)
30. (c)
31. (d)
32. (b)
33. (e)
34. (d)
35. (d)

Problems

1. (i) Nil
    (ii) BG; in the short run only
    (iii) CH
    (iv) DK
    (v) ER
    (vi) OC
    (vii) OB
    (viii) OC
    (ix) ERLD

2. (i)

Output	T.F.C.	T.V.C.	A.F.C.	A.V.C.	A.T.C.	M.C.
0	60	0	–	–	–	
1	60	50	60	50	110	50
2	60	80	30	40	70	30
3	60	105	20	35	55	25
4	60	152	15	38	53	47
5	60	225	12	45	57	73
6	60	330	10	55	65	105

    (iii) £61, £50 + £11 (approx.)
    (iv) (a) 4 (approx.)
         (b) £28 (approx.)
         (c) £35 (approx.)
         (d) 3 (approx.)
         (e) 52 (approx.)

3. (i) F
    (ii) B
    (iii) C
    (iv) A
    (v) E
    (vi) None
    (vii) D
    (viii) None
    (ix) 4
    (x) 2
    (xi) 6
    (xii) None

4. (i) 200
    (ii) £60
    (iii) £12 000
    (iv) £6000
    (v) £6000
    (vi) £50
    (vii) £4500
    (viii) 100
    (ix) £70
    (x) £1000
    (xi) (–)1
    (xii) (–)3

5. (i) 15
    (ii) 40
    (iii) 65
    (iv)

Price (£)	0	10	20	30	40	50
Supply	0	0	2	4	7	10

    (v) 13
    (vi) 10
    (vii) 3
    (viii) Nil
    (ix) $1\frac{1}{2}$
    (x) 10
    (xi) 8
    (xii) 2
    (xiii) Nil
    (xiv) 18
    (xv) 12
    (xvi) 4
    (xvii) 2

6. (i) II and VI
    (ii) None
    (iii) IV
    (iv) I
    (v) III
    (vi) V

7. (i) Perfectly competitive
    (ii) OD
    (iii) LJ
    (iv) LD/OD
    (v) ON
    (vi) OB or OE
    (vii) OA

8. (i) Sweets and Mrs. Palmer's work
    (ii) £9400
    (iii) £2000

U.K. ECONOMY

Multiple Choice

1. (i)(c), (ii)(a), (iii)(b), (iv)(d)
2. (a)
3. (e)
4. (a)
5. (c)
6. (i)(a), (ii)(c)
7. (i)(c), (ii)(e)
8. (b)
9. (d)
10. (i)(b), (ii)(c), (iii)(a), (iv)(e), (v)(d)
11. (i)(b), (ii)(d)
12. (i)(e), (ii)(c), (iii)(b), (iv)(d), (v)(a)
13. (i)(a), (ii)(c)
14. (c)
15. (b)
16. (e)
17. (e)
18. (i)(a), (ii)(i)(e), (ii)(a)

Chapter 4   Distribution: Factors of Production and their Prices

ANALYSIS

Multiple Choice

1. (b)	7. (c)	13. (e)	19. (a)		25. (d)	31. (c)	37. (c)
2. (e)	8. (b)	14. (d)	20. (i)(d), (ii)(b)		26. (c)	32. (d)	38. (b)
3. (a)	9. (b)	15. (d)	21. (c)		27. (b)	33. (c)	39. (e)
4. (d)	10. (a)	16. (i)(a), (ii)(b)	22. (d)		28. (e)	34. (b)	
5. (e)	11. (c)	17. (e)	23. (d)		29. (a)	35. (e)	
6. (d)	12. (a)	18. (e)	24. (c)		30. (b)	36. (a)	

Problems

1. (i) OG
   (ii) OA
   (iii) AKGO
   (iv) DHJKGO
   (v) DHJKA
   (vi) OB
   (vii) FG
   (viii) OC
   (ix) Either CHMA minus MEGK
        or OCHE minus OAKG
   (x) Elasticity of demand (M.R.P.)
        must be less than unity
   (xi) FG

2. (i) 30,40,45,40,35,25,15,3
   (ii) 4
   (iii) 3
   (iv) 6
   (v) 5
   (vi) 310
   (vii) Decreasing
   (viii) £20 per week

3. (i) Monopsony
   (ii) Imperfect competition (e.g. monopoly)
   (iii) AE
   (iv) OA
   (v) OA times AE
   (vi) (OWFA minus OA) times AE
   (vii) OB
   (viii) HB

4. (i) 116 000
   (ii) 134 000
   (iii) 243 000
   (iv) 1 922 000
   (v) 148 000

5. $100

6. (i) 10%
   (ii) £1123
   (iii) Buy I
   (iv) Buy neither, lend at 12%
   (v) Buy I
   (vi) £1500

U.K. ECONOMY

Multiple Choice

1. (a) (a)
2. (i)(b), (ii)(c)
3. (c)
4. (e)
5. (i)(d), (ii)(e)
6. (i)(c), (ii)(a)
7. (i)(b), (ii)(e), (iii)(e), (iv)(b)
8. (i)(b), (ii)(d)
9. (d)
10. (e)
11. (a)
12. (i)(b), (ii)(e)
13. (c)
14. (d)
15. (c)
16. (i)(c), (ii)(b)
17. (b)
18. (i)(c), (ii)(a)
19. (i)(e), (ii)(b)
20. (d)

Chapter 5   National Income

ANALYSIS

Multiple Choice

1. (e)	11. (c)	21. (i)(e), (ii)(c)	31. (d)
2. (b)	12. (a)	22. (a)	32. (c)
3. (b)	13. (b)	23. (c)	33. (d)
4. (i)(a), (ii)(d)	14. (c)	24. (i)(b), (iii)(c)	34. (d)
5. (b)	15. (d)	25. (i)(c), (ii)(b)	35. (e)
6. (a)	16. (a)	26. (e)	36. (a)
7. (e)	17. (e)	27. (a)	37. (i)(a), (ii)(e)
8. (c)	18. (d)	28. (i)(d), (ii)(c)	38. (b)
9. (c)	19. (d)	29. (e)	39. (d)
10. (a)	20. (d)	30. (i)(b), (ii)(c)	40. (a)
			41. (e)

Problems

1. (i) 20
   (ii) 5
   (iii) 6
   (iv) $1\frac{3}{4}$
   (v) $2\frac{1}{2}$

2. (i) III
   (ii) I, II, IV and V
   (iii) None
   (iv) None
   (v) I, III, IV and V
   (vi) II
   (vii) None
   (viii) I, II and III
   (ix) II
   (x) II
   (xi) V
   (xii) IV
   (xiii) None
   (xiv) I, III, IV and V

3. (i) OD
   (ii) JE/OE
   (iii) HT/BD (or HT/GT)
   (iv) LF
   (v) RJ
   (vi) Not known

4.

S	−50	−30	−10	10	30	50
C	50	130	210	290	370	450

5. (i) 160
   (ii) 560
   (iii) 520/500
   (iv) 4/5
   (v) 800
   (vi) 5
   (vii) (a) 700, (b) 1/35
   (viii) 400
   (ix) 40

6. (i) £100
   (ii) £400
   (iii) £100
   (iv) £500
   (v) +400%
   (vi) £500
   (vii) No change (±0%)
   (viii) +40%

7. (i) £8500 m
   (ii) £8500 m
   (iii) £8500 m

8. (i) £3500 m
   (ii) £3200 m
   (iii) £2700 m
   (iv) £2350 m

U.K. ECONOMY

Multiple Choice

1. (a)
2. (e)
3. (a)
4. (i)(b), (ii)(d)

5. (c)
6. (i)(a), (ii)(e)
7. (c)
8. (b)

9. (c)
10. (e)
11. (b)
12. (a)
13. (d)

Chapter 6 Money, Banking and the Price Level

ANALYSIS

Multiple Choice

1. (c)
2. (b)
3. (a)
4. (e)
5. (d)
6. (c)
7. (i)(b), (ii)(c)
8. (b)

9. (a)
10. (d)
11. (c)
12. (b)
13. (c)
14. (c)
15. (d)
16. (d)

17. (e)
18. (b)
19. (d)
20. (d)
21. (d)
22. (e)
23. (e)
24. (b)

25. (a)
26. (a)
27. (b)
28. (b)
29. (i)(e), (ii)(d), (iii)(a)
30. (e)
31. (a)
32. (d)

33. (a)
34. (b)
35. (e)
36. (c)
37. (b)
38. (c)
39. (i)(a), (ii)(e)

Problems

1. (i)

Liabilities	£	Assets	£
Deposits	600	Cash	140
		Bills	160
		Loans	300
	£600		£600

(ii) $23\frac{1}{3}\%$

(iii)

Liabilities	£	Assets	£
Deposits	1750	Cash	140
		Bills	160
		Loans	1450
	£1750		£1750

(iv)

Liabilities	£	Assets	£
Deposits	750	Cash	140
		Bills	160
		Loans	450
	£750		£750

(v) £25

2. (i) AS^2
   (ii)   At the point where AS^2 becomes vertical (i.e. AD^2 intersects AS^2)
   (iii) AS^1
   (iv) AS^3
   (v)   (a) AS^2, (b) AS^3
   (vi)   (a) AS^3, (b) AS^2

   (vii) AS^3 above full employment
   (viii) AS^2 below full employment
   (ix) AS^2 above full employment
   (x) AS^2 and AS^1 above full employment
   (xi) AS^2 and AS^1 below full employment

3.

Central bank			
	£m		£m
Bankers' a/cts	5 000	Securities	6 000
Public a/cts	4 000	Discounts + advances	5 000
Others a/cts	2 000		
	£11 000		£11 000

Joint stock banks			
	£m		£m
Deposit a/cts	19 200	Notes + coin	4 000
Current a/cts	76 800	Cash at central bank	5 000
		Money at call	10 000
		Bills discounted	5 000
		Investments	25 000
		Advances	47 000
	£96 000		£96 000

(Note: Other answers are also possible.)

4. (i) 100
   (ii) £5
   (iii) Plus 25%
   (iv) 1.6
   (v) Plus 100% (to £400)
   (vi) £2.50
   (vii) £360

5. (i) 200%
   (ii) Plus 60%
   (iii) 80
   (iv) 125
   (v) One third
   (vi) 50

6. (i) OA
   (ii) AF
   (iii) OA
   (iv) Expand aggregate demand
   (v) CB
   (vi) Shift to P^{10}
   (vii) Rise to OA
   (viii) BE (i.e. 20%) and accelerating
   (ix) OA
   (x) At F

U.K. ECONOMY

Multiple Choice

1. (i)(a), (ii)(e)
2. (d)
3. (e)
4. (d)
5. (i)(a), (ii)(b), (iii)(c)
6. (e)
7. (i)(c), (ii)(b)
8. (i)(a), (ii)(b)
9. (i)(e), (ii)(a)
10. (d)
11. (i)(c), (ii)(a)
12. (d)
13. (a)
14. (e)
15. (d)
16. (a)
17. (e)
18. (e)
19. (b)
20. (a)

Chapter 7 International Trade

ANALYSIS

Multiple Choice

1. (d)
2. (c)
3. (b)
4. (e)
5. (a)
6. (b)
7. (e)
8. (a)
9. (b)
10. (d)
11. (e)
12. (a)
13. (a)
14. (b)
15. (c)
16. (b)
17. (a)
18. (b)
19. (e)
20. (c)
21. (e)
22. (d)
23. (d)
24. (d)
25. (c)
26. (a)
27. (e)
28. (d)
29. (c)
30. (b)
31. (d)
32. (c)

Problems

1. (i) Helmets (H)
    (ii) H
    (iii) More than one sword
         (S) for 5H
    (iv) More than 5H for 1S
    (v) More than 1S for 3H
    (vi) More than 3H for 1S
    (vii) 60H + 12S
    (viii) 30H + 10S
    (ix) 36H
    (x) 4S
    (xi) 64H + 13S
    (xii) 36H + 11S
    (xiii) 4H + 1S
    (xiv) 6H + 1S
    (xv) 18H

2. (i) OA
    (ii) OW
    (iii) OR
    (iv) RW
    (v) RHGW
    (vi) Rises by AB
    (vii) Falls by VW
    (viii) Rises by RS
    (ix) Falls by RW minus SV
    (x) Falls by RHLS plus VNGW
    (xi) JKNL
    (xii) SF
    (xiii) OJ
    (xiv) OS times SF

3. (i)

Current account (£m)			
Visible trade			
Exports	245	Imports	250
Invisible trade			
Interest, etc.	15	Interest, etc.	20
Other	65	Other	30
	325		300

Capital account (£m)			
Loans received		Loans made	100
New	50		
Old (repaid)	10		
Gold outflow	15		
	75		100

    (ii) −£5m
    (iii) +£25m
    (iv) Surplus of £35m

4. (i) OC
    (ii) 1/OC
    (iii) OG
    (iv) OG times OC
    (v) CE
    (vi) OA
    (vii) OH
    (viii) OE
    (ix) OA
    (x) Buy FH francs with FH
        times OE pence

5. (i) (a) OC, (b) OE
    (ii) (a) OC, (b) OG
    (iii) OD
    (iv) OA
    (v) Almonds
    (vi) CB almonds
    (vii) OF bricks
    (viii) AB almonds and DF bricks

U.K. ECONOMY

Multiple Choice

1. (i)(e), (ii)(c)
2. (c)
3. (c)
4. (i)(b), (ii)(b)
5. (i)(e), (ii)(e)
6. (c)
7. (a)
8. (i)(b), (ii)(a)
9. (c)
10. (a)
11. (b)
12. (a)
13. (d)
14. (a)
15. (d)
16. (e)
17. (i)(a), (ii)(e)
18. (d)

Chapter 8 Economic Policy

ANALYSIS

Multiple Choice

1.	(a)	6.	(d)	11.	(c)	16.	(e)	21.	(a)	26.	(d)	31.	(a)
2.	(i)(e), (ii)(e)	7.	(b)	12.	(a)	17.	(d)	22.	(d)	27.	(b)	32.	(c)
3.	(d)	8.	(e)	13.	(e)	18.	(b)	23.	(b)	28.	(c)	33.	(c)
4.	(d)	9.	(a)	14.	(e)	19.	(c)	24.	(c)	29.	(c)		
5.	(i)(a), (ii)(b)	10.	(e)	15.	(a)	20.	(d)	25.	(e)	30.	(b)		

Problems

1. (i) II
   (ii) I
   (iii) VI
   (iv) III
   (v) None

2. (i) 40
   (ii) 200
   (iii) 120
   (iv) 2p
   (v) 3p
   (vi) £6.00
   (vii) 7p
   (viii) £12.00
   (ix) 5p

3. (i) C
   (ii) D

5. (i) 3
   (ii) 1 and 2
   (iii) 4 and 5
   (iv) 1
   (v) 5

6. (i) 3 hours
   (ii) 2 hours
   (iii) 1 hour
   (iv) 3 hours
   (v) 4 hours

7. (i) OA
   (ii) AG
   (iii) GE times OA
   (iv) OC
   (v) CN
   (vi) MN times OC
   (vii) None
   (viii) NL
   (ix) NL times OC

8. (i) £1200
   (ii) £1600
   (iii) +£50
   (iv) −£75
   (v) £600
   (vi) £1500
   (vii) Surplus of £50

U.K. ECONOMY

Multiple Choice

1.	(e)	5.	(b)	9.	(d)	13.	(c)	17.	(e)
2.	(c)	6.	(e)	10.	(e)	14.	(d)	18.	(c)
3.	(b)	7.	(a)	11.	(c)	15.	(e)	19.	(b)
4.	(i)(b), (ii)(a)	8.	(d)	12.	(a)	16.	(a)	20.	(e)